CHIAPPELLI
An American Name

Chiappelli

An American Name

Dr. Ted Chiappelli

LUMINARE PRESS
WWW.LUMINAREPRESS.COM

Luminare Press
442 Charnelton St.
Eugene, OR 97401
www.luminarepress.com

LCCN: 2020925778
ISBN: 978-1-64388-566-7

Author's Note

Thank you for your interest in reading this historical novel that I have written based on the life of my grandfather, Alfonso Chiappelli. This is a work of fiction; whereas all historical events are factual, the character of Alfonso has been superimposed into many scenes.

This is my first effort at publishing a work of fiction. I am an experienced writer, having begun my professional career as a newspaper reporter, with a shift to countless numbers of white papers, analyses, research, and academic products. I appreciate the help generously provided: first readers, Dr. Francesco Chiappelli, Lt.Col. Bruce Allen, and Elaine Trigiani; cousins who shared their photos and family tales, Valerie Vespa Killin, Linda Vespa Cessna, Rick Michelini, and Don Venturini; cousin Chris Kenney who proofread the final copy; a cousin who hosted a visit to Pistoia, Spartaco Chiappelli; and Dr. Tom Gibbon, who contributed the story written by cousin Cinda McClure Gibbon.

I have included a large number of maps, graphics and photos, and factual information such as newspaper clippings, census documents, immigration and other public records, to help make Alfonso and other people named in the novel as "real" as possible. I leaned heavily on the military histories listed in the bibliography.

I wrote this novel as a legacy to the name that I entrust to my children and grandchildren. Only one-quarter of my genealogical lineage can be traced back through Italy to the Rasenna; for my children that has been reduced to 1/8th and for my grandchildren, 1/16th—all are Chiappelli. An ancient proverb posits that children are the crown of a successful life and grandchildren are the jewels in that crown; this marks me as an incredibly wealthy man.

This novel is written for the great-grandchildren that I might never know. No matter what you are named, when you call forth that 1/32nd inner spirit it will include the Rasenna, Etruscan, Tuscany, Italian, American…Chia, Chiappore…

…the name is Chiappelli.

ENJOY

Dr. Ted Chiappelli

Bibliography

Terrain photographs and maps, American War Battlefields in Europe (78th and 80th Divisions); the American Battle Monuments Commission, John J. Pershing, chairman; 1924.

Equipment Manuals for Service in Europe, series A., No. 6; Trench Mortar Battery (motorized) equipped with 6" Newton Mortar; General Headquarters, American Expeditionary Forces; May, 1918.

Handbook of Artillery, prepared in the office of the Chief of Ordnance, Washington, DC; July, 1921.

History of the 307th field artillery, James Cameron Mackenzie, editor; 1921.

History of "A" Battery, 308th Field Artillery, 78th Division, circa 1920.

Memories of the 309th Field Artillery, William E. McCarthy, 1920.

History of 313th Field Artillery, USA; printed by Thomas Y. Crowell Company, New York; circa 1920.

** History of 315th Field Artillery edited by Regiment Committee; printed by Kohn & Pollock, Inc., Baltimore, MD; circa 1920.

42nd Division, A.E.F., Division Histories; the Digital Bookshelf, 2003.

History of the Seventy-Eighth Division in the World War, edited by Thomas F. Meehan; Mercantile Printing Company, Wilmington, DE; 1921.

History of the 80th Blue Ridge Division in World War One, Russell L. Stultz and Bill J. Krehbiel, Opinicus Publishing Co., 2015.

History of 358th Infantry, 90th Division; Gerolstein, Germany; 1 May 1919.

Maryland's 117th Trench Mortar Battery in the World War, Henry D. Stansbury; printed by the John D. Lucas Printing Company, Baltimore, MD; circa 1920.

The History of the A.E.F., Shipley Thomas; George H. Doran Company, New York; 1920.

Fire Control and Direction for Coast Artillery, lecture by Capt. Clint C. Hearn, Army School for Infantry and Cavalry, 1907.

Military Demolition, lecture by 1Lt. Douglas MacArthur, Army School for Infantry and Cavalry, 1908.

** Alfonso Chiappelli listed in roster with Battery F, Third Battalion, 315th Field Artillery Regiment, 155th Field Artillery Brigade, 80th Division.

chapter one

The name is Chiappelli. It is an American name; this is the story of exactly when and how this became so.

Chiappelli is the name of a family that originated in an Etruscan culture, survived one thousand years of Roman rule and provided a storied presence within an Italian region for another thousand years before emerging as an American saga. It would take a Great War to transform the amalgamation of this extensive history. This chapter is the story of Alfonso Chiappelli and his service in World War I. Certainly it is a story that can be replicated in every American household with modest variation. It is a tale of becoming an American.

With an active duty force of only 78,000 men—20,000 of whom were the famed Buffalo soldiers serving in all-black regiments—the United States was ill-prepared to send a fighting force to support the Allies when President Woodrow Wilson asked for a declaration of war on 2 April 1917. The National Guard provided reserve strength of 600,000 troops, presenting a wide range of readiness; even the best prepared regiments lacked modern weaponry. The industrial age had brought us to mechanized warfare. It seems ironic that with the mobilization enabled by trucks, tanks and airplanes that the fighting would get bogged down and draw stagnant in trenches, but when the Great War began on 28 July 1914 the use of these mechanical items were still newfangled ideas. On that day the U.S. Army had less than 1,000 trucks in its entire inventory.

In anticipating the call to war, military leaders had recognized the shortcomings of their armed forces and set forth to assemble a modern army that could step beyond those limitations. General Nelson Miles, he of Civil War fame and army commander in the last of the major Indian fights, spent time in his retirement years writing and advocating for the investment in trucks and roads to mechanize the American army. General John "Blackjack" Pershing used automobiles in his Mexican chase of Poncho Villa in action just prior to WWI. Leadership was well aware of the evolving opportunities for adopting advances given birth in the industrial age to applications of war. As with all new technologies, there was an acute shortage of resources; most important in this resource list was personnel who were trained in the use and maintenance of these machines.

Despite waves of patriotism sweeping the country, the call for volunteers fell far short of the initial request for a million troops. Recognizing this shortcoming, Congress passed the Selective Service Act on 18 May 1917, requiring registration of all male citizens between ages of 21 and 31. The government ordered its first draft on 5 June 1917, with three additional calls to follow. All male persons aged 21 to 30 years, inclusive, were required to register "in accordance with regulations to be prescribed by the President" or become liable to imprisonment for one year. Permitted exemptions from the draft included National and State officials, ministers of religion, theological students, military and naval personnel, county and municipal officials, mail and custom house clerks, pilots and mariners actually in sea service, artisans and workmen in armories, arsenals, and navy yards, members of sects whose creeds forbade them to engage in war, persons employed in industries and in agriculture necessary to the operations of the armed forces, those physically or mentally deficient, and those with dependents to support.

Draft boards eventually declared 24,234,021 men acceptable for military service; 4.7 million Americans were mobilized during the War, about 4 million in the Army. 2,057,675 military personnel would arrive in France; 1.4 million were combat effectives, with the remainder in logistical support.

One of those combat effectives was Alfonso Chiappelli, whose enlistment record lists him as a dark-haired, blue-eyed, 5-foot

5-inch, 21-year-old immigrant from the Ponte Della Venturina section of Granaglione, Province of Pistoia, Italy.

Alfonso had arrived in America on 18 May 1903, walking onto Ellis Island in the folds of the skirt of his mother, Giuseppina Borgognoni, along with an older brother, Dario, and infant sister, Armida. They had boarded the ship *LaChampagne* nine days earlier at LeHavre, France. In America they were met by their father (husband to Giuseppina), Egisto Chiappelli. Alfonso was 8 1/2 years old.

Family photograph of Egisto Chiappelli and Giuseppina Borgognoni made in 1903. Alfonso is standing behind his mother to the right.

In many ways Alfonso fit the stereotype of an Italian immigrant. He spoke broken English, wine was a staple served at every meal, oatmeal was something thrown to hogs for feed, and he shot his first man when he was still a teenager. Or rather, he fired his first shot, missing his intended target, hitting instead a young boy who was an innocent bystander.

Upon arrival in America, the Chiappelli family was immersed quickly into the economic segregation that kept them contained within a tight-knit Italian enclave. They settled in Freeport, Pennsylvania, a rambling collection of greenwood structures that was one of many coal towns that had sprouted in repetition along the Allegheny River, each designed with singular focus on sending a continuous flow of coal downstream to Andrew Carnegie for use in his steel plants in Pittsburgh.

In Italy Alfonso had led a somewhat structured life. He and his brother Dario attended school where they both excelled in reading and arithmetic. Daily chores were few. In typical Italian fashion his mother served his every need, forced him to attend Mass every Sunday at the Borgo Capanne Catholic Church in Granaglione, and taught him commitment to family and community. Typical of families everywhere, he spent his idle time tormenting his older brother Dario and following him into trouble, a pattern that would persist throughout his life.

He continued to trail along after Dario in his boyhood days in Freeport, roaming the back alleys, swimming 'bare ass' in the Allegheny River, fishing, and fighting. Although they could function with the rudimentary English they had acquired, it was not extensive enough for the young boys to attend the American public school. Immigrants from elsewhere in Europe who also were sponsored into America to work the black seams had their own communities; as could be expected, conflicts ensued. Despite the best efforts of his mother to keep him contained behind her skirt, she could not shelter Alfonso from the wheeling and dealing that was ongoing in the Chiappelli household.

Back in Italy, Egisto Chiappelli and wife Giuseppina Borgognoni had operated an 'osteria,' which can be best described as a bed-and-breakfast with a casual restaurant open to the public. In many ways it was a social club. A step back in their generation finds their descent from well-established Tuscan families that carried the titles Conte or Barone or Don; some were mere Maestro, but each family line was committed to a conservative agenda that promoted a social preference that kept them enriched and loyal to the Roman Catholic Church. That hierarchy had been shattered in 1861 when the independent regions and city-states united to form the Kingdom of Italy; although they were headed by a figure-head king, the newly created country quickly developed a taste for social reformation. This reconfiguration of the economic structure factored largely in pushing Egisto to America.

If marriages maintained social distinctions, the Chiappelli-Borgognoni families were decidedly part of that small rung of middle class that hung above the sharecroppers (contadino) and day laborers (giornaliero) but did not ascend to the ranks of royalty. In Tuscany there was a small noble class, a not much larger middle class, and a large majority of sharecroppers and laborers who were treated very poorly. In some locales the people might have a small plot of land or be paid a day wage by the big landowners; even so, most lived the hand-to-mouth life of a peasant. People with certain professions were considered of high standing—notary, pharmacist, doctor, or lawyer. People who practiced a trade like a carriage driver, shoemaker, miller, or ironworker were held in some esteem, sometimes referred to with the title of Maestro. When the big ironworks were in full swing or when the railroad came through Granaglione, people who were working the land flocked to those jobs to work as a bracciante (laborer).

When jobs became scarce, the bracciante looked well beyond the railroad tracks, seeing opportunity in America. The osteria became a focal point for the bracciante to discuss their options as they gathered at the card tables, drank their wine, and negotiated with the young ladies who served the meals and also were looking for their escape from the Apennine Mountains. Recruiters looking to supply labor for American coal mines targeted the osteria as a prime location from which to conduct their business; Egisto claimed a cut of the action, and he himself led at least three trips of workers in travel and job placement in America, entering once through New Orleans, taking another group via Canada, and finally leading a group of relatives and others in June 1901 through the more formal process of emigration at Ellis Island. He developed an extensive network of support within the Italian community, providing his neighborhood with protection from exploitation or extortion from those outside influences that would take advantage of newly arrived immigrants. Once settled in Freeport, as they had done back in Italy, Egisto and Giuseppina opened their home to boarders and developed their American version of an osteria.

Egisto was involved in activities that he considered informal social engagements; a vast majority of Italians, more than 90%, paid dues to the social clubs. The civil authorities in America characterized his work as criminal; to them, he was the "black hand," a catch phrase made familiar by newspaper accounts of anonymous letters sent to warn individuals who threatened the Italian community to back off. The signature on those letters often was a black hand.

The distaste that often surfaced between Italian regions surfaced in America when a Calabrian named Roberto Paira sold out the social club in Hillsville, a Pennsylvania coal town in the region west of Pittsburgh. It was not known at that time that Paira was the informant. The social club had hosted a secret gathering of miners who wanted to discuss the benefits of forming a union. A group of young boys loitering outside were playing nimbly-peg, a game where knife-throwing skills are demonstrated. The police reported that an unnamed member of the social club had been taken into custody when he was caught teaching the boys how to use a stiletto. Newspaper accounts of the 1907 raid on the social club in Hillsville reported that the police had obtained a search warrant based on sworn testimony that the "black hand" had established a school designed to train members in the use of the stiletto.

While local authorities were continuing their selective search for those whose names appeared in records taken from the Hillsville social club, Egisto used his network to secure a job with the Pioneer Coal Company. The coal company was organizing a work force to open a fresh hole into a mountainside in rural Green Township, Indiana County, Pennsylvania, near a hamlet called Shanktown. The location, steps away from the Cherry Tree & Dixonville Railroad, would mark the beginning of a drift mine that would use mining machines to track the "B" seam of coal in its flow through the earth. The family had expanded with the birth of Hugo—the first Chiappelli born in America—on 2 Jan 1907. Giuseppina delivered her fifth child—Mary Louise—on 29 Feb 1908; attending the birth was Pia Ferrari who was named godmother. The 60-mile move that would take the family to a different county would wait until Spring.

The family of Egisto Chiappelli—and the teenage years of his sons Dario and Alfonso—arrived in Starford, a company-owned hamlet of 25 houses, three stores, two churches and a school, located a mile south of Shanktown where another two dozen houses and a few stores could be found. Egisto obtained a job as a skilled operator of the mining machine and his sons signed on to provide grunt labor, pulling slags out of the coal carts to add to the bony pile. They worked the Empire "F" Mine. Although Egisto spoke only in the Tuscan version of the Italian language, he could understand the essentials of the American language and could read and write. He clearly could have written his name for the census taker who in 1910 listed the family of Agesto Gopalia as the family who had settled into one of the freshly built homes in Starford, located at 34 Rhododendron Street, with the Verardi families (brothers who married Borgognoni sisters) living next door at 44 Rhododendron. Egisto was glad for anonymity, cautioning his sons to share only what is necessary, nothing more, when dealing with civil authorities.

The houses were single-family, two-story balloon-frame construction with a gable front facing the street. These houses sat on stone foundations, with shed porches across the front and at the rear, central chimneys, and 2/2 double-hung windows. The bows and twists in the unseasoned wood siding were covered by asphalt sheathing. Houses for the mine managers were built on the same general plan but somewhat larger.

In typical Chiappelli fashion, Giuseppina took in boarders and by September 1911 Egisto had purchased from Tony Falchini for the sum of $1,100 a lot in Green Township where a hastily built structure was licensed under the mercantile permits in the "pool hall and entertainment" category. They were not alone in their economic pursuits. It would have been unusual to find any household that did not have additional members, be they boarders or relatives. Although not necessarily found on every street, it would be accurate to report that every miner had access to a "speak-easy" within a liquored stumble from his home.

Throughout his long life, Egisto had always made and maintained a rather abundant reserve of homemade wine. His American osteria attracted its crowd of regulars, mostly Italian miners since that was the language of the house. His reputation for fermenting quality wine was renowned and respect was shown for his commitment to protecting fellow countrymen from exploitation by mine owners through their company stores and from extortion by local authorities.

In Lovejoy, a coal town with about 100 houses and the rail stop just north of Shanktown, the outcry from the Caesar Forman widow could be heard proclaiming that her husband committed suicide because of a letter that she said he had received from the "Black Hand," although she conceded that her husband had other issues as well. She clearly understood that her spouse had a choice. Even after it was gently explained to him that $2 + 2 = 4$ is the same whether speaking English or Italian, arithmetic discrepancies continued to persist in the records of the company store that he had managed.

To his dying day—he lived to within months of his 100th year—Egisto could not understand why his informal affiliation with an Italian social club should lead to him and his son spending time in prison. Egisto had just gone about business the way it had been conducted for centuries in his home country. People took care of each other.

In the filing of those official documents for a property transfer and mercantile license, Egisto thought he was conforming to the American way. He was aghast when authorities charged he, wife Giuseppina, and son Dario with a list of violations. The chief witness against them—Roberto Paira; again, the name of the informant was not known at that time.

> Egisto Chiapelli with his wife, Josephine, and eighteen-year-old son, Daniel, appeared before the Court last Saturday and pleaded guilty to the charge of illegal liquor selling and permitting gambling on their premises in Starford. The father was sentenced to pay a fine of $500 and serve six months in the Workhouse; the mother was paroled in order that their six small children might be cared for and the son was sent to the Reformatory.

The Indiana Progress, Dec. 1911

Egisto was taken to the Allegheny Penitentiary in Pittsburgh. Prisoner number 48454, the last inmate received on 7 Dec 1911, was listed in the register of *"those who have been tried and sentenced to hard labor"* as age 45, dark complexion, black hair, brown eyes, 5'6" height, 162 pounds weight; occupation, storekeeper. His crime: selling liquor without a license. Six months later, he was the first prisoner released on 6 Jun 1912.

To an extent, prison was rewarding for Dario. Although his sentence was longer—one year with a $100 fine—he was taken to the Pennsylvania Industrial Reformatory in Huntingdon. The Commonwealth of Pennsylvania was among the first state governments to abolish the use of corporal punishment for crime, adopting instead a system of rehabilitation through incarceration. In 1818 the legislature provided funds for the construction of the state's first penitentiary, the Western State Penitentiary in Pittsburgh, followed by the erection of the Eastern State Penitentiary at Philadelphia in 1821.

In furtherance of the reform philosophy, the Pennsylvania Industrial Reformatory was established in 1878 to provide rehabilitation for first-offender males between the ages of fifteen and twenty-five.

Listed with the anglicized name Dan Chiappelli on the *Biographical and Descriptive Ledger* that notched inmates into the permanent records of the Huntingdon Reformatory, Dario received two intake numbers—7845 and 7874—to account for the two crimes for which he had been convicted—selling illegal liquor and common gambler, the only prisoner among 669 inmates being held for those crimes. Dario became one of 31 Italians housed at the facility, with one of the lighter sentences; the average age of inmates was 19 years with an average sentence of 5 ¾ years.

The reformatory administrators focused on building structure into the daily routines of each inmate, instituting a daily routine of exercise and military drills, with assigned chores that organized the reformatory into a self-sustaining facility. Holding to the time-proven conclusion that the major cause of crime is idle hands, inmates were schooled in trades which included painting, plumbing, carpentry and cabinetmaking, electrical, and masonry using both stone and brick. Others were assigned work in the foundry, blacksmith shop, lime kiln, brick ovens, saw mill, lumber kiln or planing mill. Classes also were provided in architectural and mechanical drawing, band and orchestra, fresco painting, and wood working.

The general superintendent noted in the *Biennial report of the Board of Managers of the Pennsylvania 1911/12* that the farm operation supplied meats, dairy, poultry and vegetables for the kitchen and that electricity generated in the power plant and water supplied by springs on the property made the Institution almost totally independent from the outside world. Inmates were assigned to apprenticeships through which they would progress until they earned their release. According to the board of managers' report, every effort was made to assess the inmate's inherent abilities in match with a chosen trade.

What the prison officials discovered in Dario was that he had an exceptional ear for music. Because his sentence was only a year, he was assigned to the band and orchestra classes where among other things he learned how to tune a piano. Dario was released the week before Christmas of 1912. (Dario spent his adult years until his death in 1950 at age 56 working in Philadelphia at Wannamaker's as a piano tuner and playing the clarinet and mandolin in Big Band orchestras that entertained speak-easies during Prohibition and after).

chapter two

Alfonso celebrated his 17th birthday as the temporary head of household in what had suddenly become a hostile environment. His labor as a slag picker was voluntary, but not all that regular. He now took his place in a line of drudgery, following the gentle slope that daily drifted foot by laborious foot deeper into the darkness of the earth. He was a coal miner. Egisto was dismissed from his position and never again would enter the mines.

Often his father had explained to him: mining is an emotional experience; coal is best produced when it is ready to move. Coal from the Empire F flowed strong; monthly outputs regularly totaled more tonnage per man than other comparable mines. Like an irregular heartbeat, massive amounts of black fragments would spew forth from the F mouth and the idle hands of the youth went to work; daily output often exceeded 500 tons. Empire F produced a coal that was considered a high-grade steam coal. The coal was shipped on the Cherry Tree & Dixonville Railroad to Cherry Tree, and then interchanged with the Pennsylvania Railroad, and shipped to Cresson and beyond for use on the railroad.

The machinery helped, but the efficiency of the Empire F Mine coal production could be attributed directly to the informal distribution of tasks to those who could perform them best, then following a formal time-proven patient process of safely preparing the work area—managing air flow, pre-positioning materials, assembling equipment, installing props. Regardless of how well they were versed in their tasks, the men would rehearse and forewarn their steps with rote communication. The men understood that when Egisto began to wrap his face with a finely woven scarf crocheted by his wife, the moment was near when he would begin to press the mining auger that he operated with the assistance of a helper into the flesh of the coal seam, beginning as close to the bottom as possible without running into rock, chopping out enough of the section of the face of coal to cause the top portion to break away from the roof, causing the black seam to tumble to the floor in an explosion of dust, arriving at an area prepared for ease of shoveling into mule-led carts that would haul the black nuggets to the surface. An oversimplified description of the mining auger would be that of an oversized chainsaw operated in a horizontal position.

The innocence of those teenage years shifted for Alfonso as it does for every male who steps into manhood with an ever expanding exploration of the world; each passing year found Alfonso stepping farther and farther away from home. "Riding the Dix" became a routine as he rode the rail line that linked the coal company towns of Commodore, Lovejoy, Starford, Shanktown, Wandin, Clymer, Dixonville and Heilwood. This was the world that Alfonso explored in his youth.

Starford was located in a rural area, but it was not isolated. It was easy to jump on one of the many railroad cars that linked coal towns up and down the tracks and led to larger population centers. Likewise, people from different parts of the world moved with the frequency of the coal in transit at the Shanktown railroad station, often bringing those who spoke Italian to the Chiappelli osteria.

It was not just the rhythm of the railroad tracks that changed on those December days of 1911. The significant emotional events forever removed whatever innocence that Alfonso might have felt. Never again would he encounter without suspicion a new arrival stepping from the train, nor a regular sitting at a gaming table in the osteria. With the removal of the "rose-colored glasses," Alfonso gained a new sense

13

of the social club; his reinterpretation of many of his life experiences served to harden his loyalty to his extended Italian family.

It is ironic that while Alfonso was learning how social order was maintained within the Italian community, concurrent to this orientation Dario was being immersed in the Anglo values of America. The surprise was measured then when the headlines in the 20 Apr 1914 edition of the local newspaper included a report that "Innocent Bystander was Shot in Fray at Starford." The report published in the *Indiana Gazette* read (sic):

> *"Robert Paira, of Starford, who was shot at and missed, at Shanktown, yesterday, by Alonzo Chipella, is being held as a witness for the trial that will occur when Chipella is captured. The two men had been drinking with a number of their friends and as is quite customary, the conclusion of the orgie ended in a quarrel, when Chipella had been refused cigarettes, Chipella drew his revolver and fired at Paira. The man, against whom the shot was directed, jumped back and escaped being shot, while the bullet entered the hip of a young boy, who had been watching the fight. Seeing the result of his anger, Chipella made good his escape before the officers arrived. Paira was taken into custody and this morning was brought to the county jail by County Constable Reed. Efforts are being made to locate Chipella and if he is captured, he will also stand trial at June court. The young boy, who took the bullet intended for Paira, is in serious condition, but it is not believed that the wound will result fatally."*

Subsequent news accounts in the *Gazette* reported that Alfonso was a fugitive who was hunted down by Constable Reed and tracked to a hideout in Heilwood. The same newspaper later bemoaned the injustice of Paira being held in the county jail, while Alfonso was scheduled for trial and let go. The news reports were accurate, to the limit of information that was provided in print.

This was one of those rare instances where the shooting can be blamed on the gun. Alfonso did pull the trigger. He was out drinking with Paira and a pack of cigarettes did drop to the table when Alfonso yelled "hand them over." The story gets a bit more complicated from there.

Earlier in that month of April 1914, Alfonso had come into possession of a 1914 model Mauser Oberndorf pistol, .32 caliber, with a walnut grip. His father admired the workmanship and German engineering applied to the instrument and said the quality could match Italian models. Egisto used the opportunity to once again note that pistols originated in their home Province of Pistoia and reminded Alfonso that his grandfather and the great generations preceding him had worked as *ferrazzoulo* and had contributed to the early development of pistols. One of the open secrets to their success was their access to quality carbon produced by the Venturini family; his sister (Aunt Rosina) was married to Alberto Venturini.

Alfonso had listened to all of those details with the impatience of youth who "know all that; you told me before." Yet he shared the information with enthusiastic pride in conversation with Paira when they met up later that Sunday night at a drinking establishment in Shanktown. Paira was a boarder in the Chiappelli household; he was single, about 10 years older than Alfonso, and was one of the first miners to rent a room not long after the family had settled in Starford.

Pistoia was a city renowned for its Renaissance-era gun-smithing, Alfonso explained, with the pistol developed some time around year 1540 so that the weapon could be fired from horseback. He noted that a pistol refers to a handgun that has a chamber integrated into the barrel, which is distinct from a revolver which has a rotating cylinder.

Starford Man Still Missing.
Alonzo Chippella, who shot at Robert Paira Sabbath, and, missing him, hit a boy who had been merely an onlooker, at Starford, is still among the missing.

Not to be outdone in the conversation, Paira launched into his own details on the history of the stiletto which also had originated in Italy. He described the stiletto as a dagger with a long slender blade and needle-like point, primarily intended as a stabbing weapon. The stiletto blade's narrow cross-section and acuminated tip reduces friction upon entry, allowing the blade to penetrate deeply. Waving his arm in mock demonstration, he gleefully shared details with Alfonso on how a stiletto would be thrust deep into the victim, and then the blade would be twisted sharply in various directions before retracting it, causing the sharp point to inflict severe internal damage not readily apparent when examining the entrance wound. He noted that the Sicilians had a *scherma di stiletto* (a school of stiletto fighting) and laughingly said that he had scared some *adolescenti* when he showed them how to use the weapon, some clicking began in Alfonso's store of remembrances.

Alfonso responded by saying that while in prison Egisto had learned that the raid in Hillsville was based on the belief that the social club had such a school. The Italian network continued to seek the member of the social club who had betrayed them to the police. It was one of those instances that stops time and removes all innocence when Alfonso casually added "you came from Hillsville," followed by the spontaneous connection of facts that marked Paira as a traitor to his people. In simultaneous response as Paira could see the information processing and awareness burst forth through Alfonso's eyes, he reached for the weapons that he had just moments before bragged were concealed in his sleeves. The table shuffled back and forth as both men sprang to their feet, with a pack of cigarettes dropping in apparent response to the yell, all accurately reported by the spectators.

Whether the gun went off by accident or intent, the trigger was pulled and Alfonso did run. He ran to the home of his uncle, Pio Chiappelli, youngest brother to Egisto, who lived in Heilwood and worked in the Greenwich Mines. Alfonso was not trying to escape authorities; he was afraid to face his mother. The youngster who was shot was his brother Hugo, 12 years his junior; the misdirected bullet had grazed his hip.

Paira had begged the sheriff to hold him in custody. The judge fined Alfonso for the discharge of a firearm in a public place, ruled the incident an accident and a family matter and dismissed the case. No further record was found on Paira.

CONTRARY TO WHAT CIRCUMSTANTIAL EVIDENCE WOULD SUGGEST, the Chiappelli was a family committed to assimilation into the American ways. There was no return to Italy for Egisto or Giuseppina although relatives did make the American visit and some of the extended family did stay. It was less a clash of cultures and more of an unforgiving learning curve in gaining an understanding of a new set of social norms and rules. Egisto was excited to have a mercantile license because that was part of the conformance. Winemaking was part of a common practice that Egisto thought was a universal routine.

Despite the age-old practices of his lifestyle, Egisto was forward thinking in embracing the modern days. Much of the mealtime discussions focused on machinery. Alfonso sometimes helped his father with the dangerous operation of the mining auger. The summer before—often he remembered that week of June in 1913—he had hopped the coal trains and rode to Windber, located in distant Somerset County, seated aboard one of the 30 flatcars loaded with steel rails to be used on extending the Pennsylvania Railroad 12 miles into the coal fields at Cairnbrook. They talked for weeks about the gigantic steam shovels that Alfonso had watched in operation as the roadbed was pounded into shape to support laying of tracks from Mine 39.

On this day the discussion also was focused on machinery; specifically, automotive repair. The number of vehicles licensed for operation on American roads had been doubling every other year for the last 10 years, now numbering 1.75 million cars and 100,000 trucks. The time was opportune for Alfonso to matriculate to Pittsburgh and enroll in those courses being taught by Westinghouse in automotive repair. This had long been of interest to Alfonso beginning the day he had first read about the competition the Westinghouse Corporation was engaged in for a military contract to develop a truck that could operate under harsh conditions.

It also was time for the Chiappelli family to move. Although each family member had encountered harsh life-altering events, their days in Starford were not unkind. The rural tight-knit community was supportive through all of their travails, but now that closeness was a bit too familiar.

Alfonso recalled with satisfaction the thoughtful planning that he had observed when he had walked through Cairnbrook that year past. He took special note of the infrastructure such as water lines and electricity, along with designated streets and a thoroughfare for the 85 houses and stores that were in different phases of construction. The collection of company housing constructed to support operations of the Loyalhanna Coal and Coke Company was slated to grow to more than 200 homes when the Berwind-White Coal Mining finished opening their mines in this coal field. Loyalhanna had spent more than $1.5 million in establishing the mining village.

The area was destined to grow to an even larger metropolitan area as just one mile farther down the tracks a real estate boom was underway in a borough incorporated as Central City, named for its central location on the proposed extension of an eastern railhead.

The Chiappelli family was among the first to purchase tickets to Cairnbrook when the railroad opened its tracks for passenger service in the fall of 1915. The major changes that Alfonso observed in the development of the town since his previous visit were that a freight depot had been erected at the Cairnbrook station and a National Bank had been established.

They laughed at a newspaper report that Cairnbrook was "many miles from nowhere, and the lonesomest place imaginable." For the Chiappelli, the town was a vibrant opportunity to start a new life in America, marked by the new life that was growing in Giuseppina as her pregnancy began to show. That the family would be welcomed into the community was not at issue as the arrival of each passenger train at 7:30 a.m. and 1:40 p.m. daily was met with recruiters; there was an acute shortage of miners.

The family planned to be moved by Spring 1916. Egisto arranged for the purchase of a small well-constructed stone house at the edge of a hamlet called Middletown, located at the beginning of the north mountain ridge from which he could see beyond the Shade Creek Valley where Cairnbrook and Central City had been seeded, to the rich game lands that lay beyond as a public treasure. The scene was reminiscent of the Villa di Cireglio, the mountainside hamlet of homes that overlooked Pistoia and the valley beyond, the place where Egisto was born and where the Chiappelli had lived for more than 500 years.

On 2 Feb 1916, Alfonso walked into the Indiana County courthouse and emerged as a naturalized citizen of the United States.

Later that month Egisto recorded the death certificate for the stillborn child he had buried in the back yard. With bittersweet memories, the Chiappelli moved on from life at Starford.

The family was absorbed quickly into the chaotic activity of constructing a coalmine town in the middle of nowhere within a few short years. Their community now was a mix of ethnicities, with Italians numbering few among the larger mix of Eastern European immigrants, mostly Slavs from a long list of countries such as Poland, Slovakia, and Slovenia.

Egisto and Giuseppina were no longer in the osteria business. Egisto continued to make wine in large volume and their home continued to be a social club as it was open to the community. A large barrel set on the porch where letters gathered from the post office were tossed in batches to be sorted for neighbors and friends. Next door was Otis Motis Hall, a well driller. A few houses away on the other side, at the corner of the dirt trail that was designated the Ridge Road, was the local butcher Jozef Milavec. Egisto regularly tossed his leavings from wine fermentation over the fence to the cattle that stood next in line for the slaughter house; Milavec did not mind as it seemed to have a calming effect on his cows.

By the time Alfonso was drafted, he was a seasoned miner with the Loyalhanna Company. He also had begun to tinker with cars, doing repairs when he was not in the mines. On occasion he would be assigned to work on company time on the automobiles owned by the mine superintendent or a mine manager. Alfonso had his own jalopy, a collection of parts that mostly originated at the Buick production plant. The day he received his orders, he dug into the hillside that sloped away from their Middletown house, creating a three-sided pit that he could drive into, installing a flat roof overtop, and prepared his car for long-term storage, not knowing when he would return.

Alfonso was a reluctant participant in WWI. When he registered for the draft on 5 June 1917, he requested exemption status claiming his mother and father as his dependents. His older brother, Dario, claimed his youngest brother (Hugo) and sister (Mary) as his dependents; Dario was not selected for service. The first draft lottery was held 20 July 1917 to select 1,374,000 men for examination to provide 687,000 men in the first increment of troops; 10,500 numbers were drawn, with 258 the first number. The combination of numbers that resulted in selection included 21 Dec 1894, the day Alfonso was born.

Alfonso was inducted to serve in the National Army on 4 Oct 1917 at Somerset, Pennsylvania. He was in the first wave of a draft that was expected to fill 117 Army regiments authorized in the National Defense Act of 1916.

chapter three

World War I forced fundamental changes in the organization of the United States Army. The infantry division remained the primary fighting unit, but its organization was greatly revamped based on British and French experiences in trench warfare and the limited availability of trained officers. Firepower, supply, and command and control became paramount; column length or road space no longer controlled the size and composition of the infantry division. The Allies advised that the Army should not send a large cavalry force to France; horses and fodder would occupy precious shipping space, and the Allies had an abundance of cavalry.

Gen. Blackjack Pershing led the reorganization of the Army through the General Organization Project which prescribed an infantry division of 25,000 men consisting of two infantry brigades. Each brigade would have two infantry regiments and one three-company machine gun battalion. The division also would have a field artillery brigade comprised of one 155-mm howitzer regiment, two 3-inch gun regiments, and one trench mortar battery. Logistic support for each division was organized through trains of military police, ammunition, supply, ambulance, field hospital, engineer, and headquarter units.

The War Department published tables of organization on 8 August 1917 that became known as the "square division." The design almost doubled the number of troops in a division from the previous organizational structure. The strategic thinkers at the War Department recognized that the lack of experienced divisional-level officers and staffs made a smaller number of larger divisions more practical. The division was to field enough men to fight prolonged battles so as to avoid getting mired down in the trenches. The number of men in a division was increased to 28,000 to accommodate increased workloads assigned to officers who were expected to balance both administrative and operational tasks. The supply train was motorized, and the ammunition and ambulance trains were equipped with both motor- and horse-drawn transport. The trench mortar battery was assigned to the field artillery brigade to provide high-angle fire.

There were to be three components to the Army, distinguishing the already formed Regular Army and National Guard (reserve) units from the draftees who were intended to fill newly organized National Army units. Divisions were to be numbered 1 through 25 for the Regular Army, 26 through 75 in the National Guard, and 76 and above in the National Army. Blocks of numbers for infantry and field artillery brigades were reserved with 1 to 50, Regular Army; 51 through 150, National Guard; and 151 and above, National Army.

In an effort to promote unit cohesiveness and politically to maintain popular support, draftees were assigned to specific units based on geographic location. There was no other system for classifying new recruits as they entered the service. Officers and top enlisted men were chosen for the "first five percent;" these were mostly volunteers who were to comprise the first 1,400 men assigned to a division (5% of the 28,000 man contingent).

Orderly confusion reigned across the nation as military camps sprang to life in replication of dusted-off readiness plans. The pattern was repeated. Acquire a large acreage of open flat land—a peanut farm in Virginia, training grounds in Maryland, or a pine forest in New Jersey—and install an infrastructure to support a population of 50,000. The plans for each camp as prepared in Washington D.C. provided for a huge U-shaped cantonment, with barracks on both sides, store-houses, and shops at the bend in the U and spacious parade grounds within the enclosure.

In June 1917 at 26 sites across the United States, roads were being graded and ditches dug, followed in short order by the installation of water, sewage, and electrical grids. Buildings appeared seemingly haphazardly as the 'almost done' began to clash with the 'just begun' phases of construction. The development followed a prioritized list of logistical support needed to receive and process the men in an orderly fashion—food, clothing, shelter. The first barracks were available just in time to house the officers who began arriving the last days of August from their 12-week training programs at established military locations such as Madison Barracks in New York and Fort Myer in Virginia. Orientation to artillery would have included battlefield tactics written by Clint C. Hearn and Douglas MacArthur, two officers whose command decisions would indirectly impact the role Alfonso was to play.

The majority of the barracks, which were being erected at a rate of 15 a day, were soon occupied by men of the new National Army whose arrival beginning on 6 Sep 1917 swelled camps to their capacity when by October the full complement of draftees called in the first wave were to have reported. Each barracks accommodated 200 men. They were two-story wooden structures, with the main floor used for the kitchen, mess-hall, offices, storerooms, and sleeping quarters. The upper floor was for sleeping quarters only. Each barracks had its own outside latrine. Officers, of course, had separate quarters and latrines.

Alfonso was at the tail end of that first wave. Without fanfare, he picked up a bundle that included a winter jacket, sandwiches, and a bottle of wine, in addition to the lengthy list provided by a correspondent to the Pittsburgh newspapers who advised that new National Army men reporting to Camp Lee provide themselves with the following articles "so as to be secure against possible delays and discomforts: an improvised bed sack, into which straw can be stuffed; three suits of underwear; three or more pairs of socks; two or more soft shirts; broad toe shoes; an extra old, clean suit of clothes; and a liberal supply of food. " The correspondent further advised that trains might be delayed and that it would be days before uniforms were handed out. In the meantime, the nights will be cold.

He said goodbye to his family who had gathered on the porch. A bit chagrinned because he usually drove his car, Alfonso waved to the few neighbors who also watched as with purposeful steps he tread down the road to the Cairnbrook rail station to catch the 0730 train to Windber. A few acquaintances who had been loitering at the depot shouted their support as he boarded the passenger car, but most spectators quietly watched, some in relief that their number had not been called.

In his step onto the train, Alfonso had been welcomed with an exaggerated invitation to sit with Harry Lambert who had boarded the train in Central City. Harry also was on his way to the war. Alfonso was struck with surprise that his first encounter with a fellow draftee would offer such a contrast in conscripts. Harry was about the same age as Alfonso. He farmed a section of family-owned land which could be seen on the mountain ridge that sat opposite of the Chiappelli front porch. The main thoroughfare through Cairnbrook had been named McGregor Avenue to acknowledge that the town was built on land that had been purchased from Jacob McGregor, an uncle to Harry. The families were among the earliest settlers of the Shade Creek Valley. This trip was one of the few times Harry Lambert had ever left his farm.

The contrast also must have been obvious to the draft board members. Harry Lambert had been selected to fill a vacancy in the National Guard unit from Somerset whose members had departed in unison in early September, marching off to the cheers of a patriotic parade. For Harry and Alfonso, it was the trees standing at attention, waving flags of color—red from the maple, yellow from the ash, orange from the oak—that provided their send-off. Alfonso uncorked his bottle of dandelion wine, his father's favorite, and offered a toast to their survival; Lambert appreciated the gesture with a nervous chuckle and quick swig.

Alfonso closed his eyes as he savored the taste of springtime and honey in the wine and for those few seconds he drifted away to one of his happiest recollections of life. It was a rite of Spring for the Chiappelli children to dance through the fields as they filled a bushel basket with the bright yellow tops of dandelions. He envisioned the youngsters, Hugo and Mary, giggling with delight as their fingertips turned black from pulling the yellow petals free of the green capsule that held them together, reducing the collection of dandelions to a gallon-size pack that his father would place in a 5-gallon crock along with oranges, lemons and raisins. Egisto followed a well-rehearsed recipe that aged with the step of the seasons. First he would bring water and sugar to a boil, dissolving the sugar. While the liquid was cooling, he would squeeze the juice of the oranges and lemons over the dandelion pedals and then use his pocket knife to chop the rinds into fine shavings. He would add this mix into the crock along with raisins and egg whites. He then would pour the now lukewarm sugar water over the ingredients, add a measure of rehydrated yeast, and cap the container. After a month of fermenting, Egisto would siphon the wine into a clean container topped with an airlock, leaving the sediment behind and allowing for a secondary fermentation for another two months. The wine was then ready for bottling, preceded by ample taste testing. Alfonso laughed with the thought that one of his earliest recalls of rote memorization was the recipe for a one-gallon batch:

- 3 quarts, water.

- 1 quart, dandelion pedals.

- 3 pounds, sugar.

- 2 fist-size oranges.

- 2 fist-size lemon.

- ½ pound, raisins.

- 1 egg white.

- 1 cake yeast packet.

Alfonso was jolted from his revelry as the train screeched to a stop. Harry changed trains in Windber, as he headed for Camp Meade in Maryland. Alfonso Chiappelli was on his way to Camp Lee in Petersburg, Virginia.

If he suffered any delusion that he would feel a sense of belonging in being called to serve his new nation, it was quickly dismissed when Alfonso was separated from other men selected from Somerset County, Pennsylvania. Contingents of men from Pennsylvania were grouped to fill assigned units at Camp Meade, Maryland. The unit histories from both Camp Dix and Camp Meade are replete with examples of efforts to keep out of their units men who spoke broken English or looked different. Alfonso fit both categories. Although he had arrived in America with a functional command of the English language, his residency in the States for just over a dozen years had not removed his accent. His induction papers noted his dark complexion and he was classified as a 'darkie.'

He was not alone in being singled out. Asians were moved to menial jobs because the gas masks would not seal across their noses. Bigots were quite vocal in their dislike of meals being prepared and served by Negroes; labor shortages due to the wartime draft had made them the only hands available. The history for one artillery battery recorded this notation about men being transferred into the unit:

> "...we received forty brilliant men from Camp Upton, most of their names ending in 'ski,' such as Solinski, Coslopski, etc. In due time, however all were eliminated and only nine Irishmen were assigned to the Battery."

At the train station in Johnstown, Alfonso was grouped with a collection of other draftees who had been assigned to Camp Lee. Although the men were as varied as the collection of suitcases, valises, satchels, and bundles they were carrying, a common theme began to emerge. Many were recently arrived immigrants who had worked in the steel mills or coal fields.

They were met at the train station in Petersburg by a drill sergeant who gave them their first taste of military order when he shouted them into a loose formation for the walk to camp. Although they had not eaten a meal since beginning their journeys, the first order of business for the men was to carry and place steel cots, clean barracks, and put every item in an assigned place that would be standard in each building throughout the encampment. After a meal, a lecture, and a warning not to leave the area came the first sleep of a soldier. A shrill whistle reminiscent of the mines sounded the arrival of morning. The men were herded into lines, answered to roll call, dismissed for mess, and then pressed into formation for processing through the mustering office.

"Each man answered to his name, as it was called in alphabetical order," Alfonso wrote in his letter home, "and upon entering was politely informed to discard his wearing apparel. Father Adam had nothing on us as we passed in line before the doctors for our first physical examination. Several hours later we emerged, thoroughly examined, inoculated, branded finger prints taken, and bound indefinitely to the service of the United States Army."

Alfonso was placed with Battery F, 315th Field Artillery Regiment, 155th Field Artillery Brigade, 80th Division. He was tasked with manning a 155mm caliber howitzer cannon. Each Brigade had one heavy artillery regiment and two light artillery regiments, each with a complement of 200 men. The 155mm howitzer was the heavy artillery and the 75mm howitzer was the light. Each regiment had six batteries, with each battery manned by two dozen newly designated soldiers who most likely had never before seen such a weapon.

The day following began a routine of physical exercise drills in the morning, followed by a long walk, with afternoons devoted to lectures and instruction on ballistics and the use of artillery and trench mortars in warfare. The men were still dressed in their civilian garb and practicing with pretend artillery, four wooden replicas built with hollowed out logs mounted on wagon wheels, as the November winds suggested snow.

Alfonso had been befriended by Samuel E. Adams, a mountain man from Shuff, Virginia, who had worked the coal fields of southwestern Virginia. "Lose the accent," Sam advised, "or don't talk." He explained in graphic detail how black men were treated in the South and he did not want Alfonso to be misidentified as a negro, even if his enlistment documents seemed to describe him as such. Alfonso laughed this off until his first weekend pass into Petersburg; after that, it was not so funny.

Sam was related to a contractor who had been awarded a large chunk of the work to build the roads on Camp Lee. While most of the men applied their free time toward seeking entertainment in nearby Petersburg, Alfonso and Sam secured jobs at the construction site, with Sam assisting Alfonso in repairing and maintaining the fleet of trucks and other construction equipment.

This arrangement was frowned upon by a shave-tail lieutenant who brought Sam and Alfonso up on charges of AWOL (absent without leave). In mocking tones he mimicked an Italian accent and said that Alfonso had told him "me no lika your job, one dollar a day—me gotta better job now, paya three dollars a day." This was the same young Southern officer who demanded that troops be banned from a number of establishments in Petersburg because they served Negroes; the city had a large black population.

The lieutenant regularly complained that the Italians gave him considerable trouble. "They just will not stay in their respective barracks," he complained. "If they have a pal in another battery, they go over to spend the night, and when finally rounded up they innocently reply: "Me no lika your hotel; me sleepa with a ma friend.""

"These men are not your slaves," the more seasoned Colonel Ferris responded when the lieutenant pressed the issue. "They are entitled to their time." Still, with much of the work in clearing the roads being accomplished by the soldiers as part of their assigned duties, the veteran officer was reluctant to establish a precedent. The charges were reduced to a reprimand with an agreement that Sam and Alfonso would donate half of their earnings to the Second Liberty Loan. Battery F earned highest honors for subscriptions, helping the Regiment commit $96,000 to the fund drive, subscribing $75 for each man in the unit.

Leaves and furloughs for five days were granted to all men and officers over the Christmas holidays. Alfonso also received a transfer to Camp Dix, New Jersey, with assignment to the 303rd Trench Mortar Battery. Uniforms had finally arrived and had been distributed in the weeks just prior to that Christmas break and Alfonso stood with Sam for a photograph prior to his departure.

Alfonso later learned that the 80th had been named the "Blue Ridge Division" by its commander, Major General Adelbert Cronkhite, a career officer who had lectured in military science at the academy. In naming the division, MGen. Cronkhite overruled his second-in-command who had been advocating Lee Division as the name. Cronkhite privately admonished that he would not lead a Division named for a traitor and who had lost his war. He was a northern who was tired of the Southern attempt to rewrite history; "you lost, get over it" he would tell those who dared challenge the Union. In making his announcement, the General said:

> "As the men of the Division come from the three States of Pennsylvania, Virginia, and West Virginia, it was desired that some name should be decided upon that would apply equally to each of the three Commonwealths mentioned. If you will look at a map of the United States, you will notice that the three States are joined by the chain of mountains known as the Blue Ridge. . . As the Blue Ridge mountains

are the inanimate, geographical thread of union, so the Blue Ridge Division, with the best men of the three great States fighting side by side in the same glorious cause, will be the animate, living thread of union. The slogan selected for the Division is `Vis Montium,' which, translated from the Latin, is `Strength of the Mountains.'"

chapter four

Instructions from the War Department were provided to maintain a system of localization of divisional units, concentrating draftees into the National Army based on their geographic location. The written exception to this policy was "Other units of the division to be organized by transfer of qualified men, irrespective of the locality of their origin." It was the technicality of that sentence that had a profound effect on Alfonso. While the system of localization had many points in its favor, the obvious defect was identified and a process of assigning men according to their qualifications was adopted.

Alfonso was assigned to the 303rd Trench Mortar Battery, 153rd Brigade, 78th Division. His assignment to this unit was due as much as by happenstance as an accident of fate. Army planners had recognized the need to mechanize the artillery; in order to build the resources to support this effort, the Army had let contracts for developing training manuals of personnel and repair manuals for equipment. One of those contracts went to Westinghouse, Inc., with a proving ground established just south of Pittsburgh. The project was under the direction of Sergeant Major John Edward McGlothan, recently returned from the Mexican Expedition. McGlothan was career Army, having entered the enlisted ranks in 1902, back-dating his birth year of 1885 by one. Although he always maintained a tidy appearance, McGlothan was more practical and precise than spit and polish. He left Westinghouse with not only manuals, but also rosters of students who had enrolled in the automotive repair courses that had been offered.

McGlothan could have been sent to the 12-week finishing school and been commissioned an officer, but that would have been followed with a command assignment locking him into a structured chain-of-command with corresponding defined duties. As the senior enlisted advisor reporting directly to the Artillery commander, he would have greater flexibility.

McGlothan was handpicked for his assignment by Gen. Blackjack Pershing, with specific instructions to detail the role of enlisted support for a mechanized artillery. McGlothan was a quick study, reflected by his quick rise through the ranks, seeing firsthand the benefit of mechanic mobilization in chasing Poncho Villa through the northern plains and mountains of Mexico and retaining lessons learned. Those lessons began with the mobilization of artillery on trains that presented this force as a fighting entity separate from the infantry. McGlothan foresaw the deployment of artillery as an offensive tactic, but understood the need to achieve integration with the infantry to be effective.

This conclusion was enthusiastically embraced by Brigadier General Clint Calvin Hearn, commander of the 153th Field Artillery Brigade. In his 1894 paper *Fire Control and Direction for Coast Artillery,* Hearn had advocated delegating command of trench mortar batteries to front-line commanders who could exercise judgment to deploy the weapons as needed. In order to make effective the new technologies available in modern armament, he explained, it is necessary to have men and equipment to provide range and communication. "The first step is to get information; the second, to transmit it to the place where it is used," Hearn lectured, concluding, "third, to use the information intelligently when it is received." Past use of trench mortars assigned them to fix positions; Hearn maintained that with the advent of high-powered and rifled mortars, the batteries could become mobile.

THE WINTER OF 1917 WAS EXCEPTIONALLY COLD UP AND DOWN the East Coast, with diseases rampant due to the large movement of people as the nation geared up for war. The streets of the Camp Dix were nearly deserted the day in early January 1918 when Alfonso walked from the train station to the barracks assigned to the 303rd Trench Mortar Battery; due to the duplication in camp layout he instinctively knew the location when the guard at the entrance gate provided directions. At that particular moment there were only about 7,000 men on base; another 5,000 troops were away on leave or convalescing. The remainder of the 25,000 soldiers who had reported to Camp Dix by mid-October—about 13,000 men who were mostly members of the National Guard—had been shipped to Europe for replacement in Regular Army divisions. Although the men left behind had begun to call their new home "Camp Delirious," Alfonso began to see the Army as more of an opportunity and less of a threat. Nevertheless, he was under no disillusion that he was anything more than a disposable part.

From 10 Jan to 20 Feb, battery A of the 307th was quarantined because of an outbreak of measles; another battery was quarantined for mumps. In the early part of February a much dreaded epidemic of influenza broke out and the men were all confined to their barracks, venturing in public only if they were wearing a gauze mask. Four men died.

His transfer to the 303rd had been accompanied by a promotion. Alfonso was now a Private First Class, which meant that his chewings out would come directly from Sergeant Major McGlothan to whom he would report. There was no measure of like or dislike in the Sergeant; he was focused on the accomplishment of the assigned task and indifferent to personalities. Alfonso took no offense; for him it was a sense of belonging, an awareness that he had something of value to contribute to the war effort. His mother was fond of saying "make yourself a person of value, success will follow." It was a quote from Albert Einstein. He had lost faith in that sentiment at Camp Lee when in his mix with the mountain men of the Virginias, he and a handful of other Pennsylvania miners were among the few who could read and write, yet their ability was treated with distain by many of the southern officers appointed over them. "We will do the readin' and writin'," one of them laughed, "and you do the shootin' and dyin'." If would have been funny if he was not so sincere.

The daily grind was still monotonous; materials were scarce, the parade grounds a sea of mud, and the firing range always a cold distant hike. Alfonso approached his assignments with no greater measure of enthusiasm, but he did pay far more attention to details and had a greater awareness of the hustle and bustle in his surrounds.

Alfonso had seen such hurried construction at his every move in America, but nothing on the scale of Camp Dix and with such conformance to order. It was especially impressive to recognize that within three months there was a railroad system with sidings, spurs, freight houses and stations; a complete system of surfaced roads for the entire camp; a water system with a 16-inch main, bringing water a distance of 8 miles, and 20 additional miles of mains; a complete fire department; buildings to house the troops; a cold storage and refrigerating system; store houses for food, clothing, and military supplies; hospitals, bakeries, salvage, clothing and shoe repair shops, complete installation of a camp telephone system, and finally, a complete electric lighting system.

In addition to the infrastructure, Alfonso was impressed that the Army was sensitive to the social needs of the men and proved amenities that built the Camp into a complete community. The camp had a theatre, moving picture houses, dance halls, libraries, hotels, railroad station, post office, local regimental stores or exchanges, electric light and telephone systems, newspaper, taxi service, and numbered streets and avenues, and Military Police to direct all the traffic.

One of the many problems that confronted the Division authorities from the very beginning was the continual stream of visitors that almost daily wended their way to camp, often gathering at the shooting range and parade grounds to watch the Army show its muscle. So great did the weekend traffic become that autos had to be parked outside the limits of camp and the journey through camp made on foot, with the greatest crowds drawn to the arrival of the *Brittania*, the prototype for a British tank. The demonstration began with the tank pounding through a trench-strewn field, followed by a bulldozing through an old barn. The tank then punched headlong into a snow-covered sand bank that had gathered a six-foot high perpendicular bed of ice, where the tank promptly bounced upside down with the treads rolling around like a turtle flopping its legs. Alfonso laughed; McGlothan frowned.

On through the bleak cold winter months that followed, the battery labored with half the quota of troops. The winter was extraordinarily severe for New Jersey, therefore as many drills as possible were carried on inside the barracks. By the end of February, the final increment of the first draft had arrived and training work was speeded up.

Daily, often wearing gas masks, the men practiced their steps: unpacking the trench mortar from the truck, pre-positioning supplies, assembling the weapon, establishing communication with command, obtaining coordinates, simulating firing shells selected from the stockpile per order, securing weapon, taking inventory of supplies, disassembling the trench mortar and repacking the truck.

36

McGLOTHAN HANDED TO ALFONSO A MANUAL PROVIDED BY the Office of the Chief of Ordnance, War Department, Washington, D.C, for the 58mm Trench Mortar, a weapon purchased from the French. "Memorize this," was the simple direct command given. He did.

"*The piece is divided into four plain parts: the mortar proper, the carriage, the bed, the platform.*

The parts of the mortar proper are: the barrel, of steel with a smooth bore of 58.3mm (2.29 in.); the breech end; the elevating band with two elevation locking bolts, washers, and wing nuts for clamping the mortar at the proper elevation; and the firing mechanism adapter, screwed into the breech end.

The carriage consists of two cast iron cheeks, each with a slotted guide for the elevation bolts; a trough into which the cheeks fit; the axle, which is inserted through holes in the trough, the cheeks, and through the breech end of the mortar; and the elevating mechanism. This elevating mechanism consists of a steel oscillating support, threaded internally with a left-hand thread, a bronze elevating hand-wheel on a bronze screw threaded externally with a left-hand thread to fit the oscillating support and internally with a right-hand thread of twice the pitch. A steel screw, threaded to fit the right-hand thread of the bronze screw, is fastened by a pin to a small yoke

on the elevating band of the mortar. The oscillating support is fastened by two bolts through the slotted guides of the two cheeks of the carriage. The back part of the trough consists of a high circular plate on the back of which is bolted a steel piece carrying a lug and the traversing clamp screw. The trough is provided at the front with two transportation rings and at the back with two traversing rings.

The bed consists of five oak timbers, two short and three long, the latter being fastened together at the front by a channel iron and bolt through the middle of each timber. The middle bolt carries a clamp for holding the front of the trough to the platform. At the back the five timbers are held together by the back plate, which is sunk into the wood to a depth of 1.5 centimeters (0.6 in.) and fastened with five bolts, one in the center of each timber. The base of the back plate is provided at the front with a row of thirty traversing holes, one inch between centers. The rear surface of the back-plate is divided into eighty equal divisions, each graduation having a value of ten mils, the horizontal field of fire being 800 mils. The middle point of each division is marked by a dot, and each hundred mils is stamped with the figures. The right-hand edge of the lug of the circular plate is used as the index with these graduations in setting the mortar in direction. The center board of the bed carries a pivot projecting one centimeter (0.4 in.) above the wood. This fits into a hole in the under surface of the trough, and is the pintle center of the piece. This pivot is 60 centimeters (23.6 in.) in front of the face of the back-plate, which is curved to this radius.

The platform is not always used, but it is employed where the soil offers very little stability, and always for the firing of heavy bombs. The platform consists of eight cross timbers held together by two long angle irons between which the bed is placed. Near the front of the platform are bolted two small angle irons which hold the front of the bed firmly in place. The rear timber is shod with a channel iron. Two clamps *are provided on the front timber and three on the back for holding down the bed. Each timber has a ring at each end to facilitate handling.*

parts	*weight-lbs.*
Mortar:	
Barrel	100
Breech-End	53
Elevating Band and Wing Nuts	13
Carriage:	
Cheeks	286
Trough	132
Elevating Mechanism	13
Axle	66
Bed:	
Back Plate	130
Middle Timber with Channel Iron	77
Long Timbers	123
Short Timbers	26
Under Platform:	
Front Timber	114
Second Timber	66
Plain Timbers	309
Back Timbers	160
Channel Iron	110
Angle Irons	101
total weight for piece—*with platform*	1879
total weight for piece—*without platform*	1019

When officers assembled for commander's call, McGlothan always had a seat at the table. He was present the night of 4 May when BGen Hearn gave notice that the division had received orders to ship out to France and he was a member of the advance team from headquarters that left the morning of 6 May in a group that included BGen Hearn, his Battery Commanders, several Lieutenant aides, and about 40 men.

On Friday, May 17th, all conjecture was set aside, all drills ceased, and Camp Dix was closed to visitors, "a necessary procedure lest any information of our time and place of sailing might find its way into unworthy hands," Alfonso wrote in his last letter sent home.

In order to keep as many people away as possible, no tickets were sold by railroads leading into Camp Dix.

Alfonso received his official notice when the blast of a bugle startled him from a deep sleep at 2200 hours (10 p.m.) on 22 May. The men emptied the barracks and quietly stood outside as the silence of the night was broken in whispers as word spread that the 153rd Field Artillery Regiment would start overseas on Saturday, 25 May 1918.

Barrack bags were stacked and loaded into trucks for transport. Alfonso drove a truck that provisioned the 303rd Trench Mortar Battery, pulling his vehicle into a convoy line headed for the docks at Philadelphia, where the equipment was crammed into assigned space aboard an American ship, the *Arrawa*. Although the Regiment was designated as "motorized," the number of assigned vehicles were few. The quartermaster had trucks to move his supplies, the commander had his chauffer and staff car, the heavy artillery had two caterpillar tractors to share with its six batteries, and the Mortar Battery had its specially designed Packard truck.

THE DAY BEFORE LEAVING ALFONSO HAD ONCE AGAIN INVENtoried the list of items for which McGlothan had made him personally responsible. The list was straight from the manual:

LIST OF FRENCH MATERIEL FURNISHED A BATTERY OF 58 MM. No.2 TRENCH MORTARS, EACH COMPRISING:

1 Barrel.

1 Elevating band.

2" washers.

2 wing nuts.

1 Elevating hand nut.

1 Cheek, right.

1 Cheek, left.

1 Trough.

1 Axle.

1 Elevating mechanism.

1 Firing mechanism, percussion.

1 Platform, small.

1 Stake, iron, platform.

1 Wrench, socket, double ended.

1 Under platform.

12 SERVICE BOXES, EACH CONTAINING:

1 Sledge hammer.

1 Pliers, pair.

1 File, triangle.

1 Mallet, wooden.

1 Extractor hook.

1 Vinyl cleaner.

1 Brass brush.

1 Brace.

1 Bit, screw driver.

3 Levers, wooden.

4 1/2 nags, kilos.

1 Flashlight.

1 Holster, quadrant.

1 Belt, holster, quadrant.

1 Case, wood, quadrant.

1 Padlock.

1 Lever, traversing iron.

1 Rule, meter, folding.

1 Emery cloth, 1/2 meter.

1 String, 3 mm., 1/~ kilo.

1 Lanyard.

1 Quadrant.

1 Can, oil, containing 1/4 liter oil.

1 Box, grease, containing 1 (1/2 lb.)
    kilo heavy grease.

ACCESSORIES:

6 Tongues, metal, towing carts.

6 Singletrees, cart.

10 Pins, picket large.

10" pins small, cart.

G Shafts, cart.

50 Bags, trace.

4 Pails, grease.

10 Ropes, lashing.

6 Battery bags.

12 Lanterns, candle.

6 Sheets, drawing paper.

1 Periscopic alidade.

1 Rule.

1 Scale, meter.

1 Box, "Accessory."

4. Paulins, wagon, escort.	20 Lanterns, kerosene.	1 Box, tool.
12 Paulins, 3 X 4 meters.	20 Candles, packages (1 doz. to package).	1 Protractor, celluloid.
72 Traces, cart.	22 Field glasses.	12 Pencils, colored.
144 Hauling ropes.	1 Periscopic goniometer.	3 Pencils, drawing.
30 Padlocks and keys.	1 Tripod, periscopic goniometer.	1 Ink, red, bottle.
50 Thongs, leather, axle pin.	1 Case, periscopic goniometer.	1 Ink, blue, bottle.
10 Traces, cart, extra.	12 Sheets, tracing paper.	1 Tripod, plane table.
100 Tacks, thumb.	tongs.	1" pump.
1 Leveling alidade.	cold chisels.	2" oil cans.
1 Compass, drawing.	anvil cutter.	1" horn.
1 Tape, decimeter.	1 Declinator, plane, table.	1 Chest, signal, containing
1 Square.	2 Screws, declinator.	3 Lights, signal.
1 Plane table.	1 Extension bar, drawing, compass.	3 Batteries, sets in leather cases.
1 Eraser.	1 Bicycle.	12 Batteries.
1 Pen, drawing.	1" lantern.	1 Bulb, extra.
rods.	1" tool box.	
palette.	1" inner tube.	

The site for Camp Dix had been selected because it was a short distance from more than one point of demarcation; 30 miles from Philadelphia and less than 100 miles to New York. Men from the light artillery units traveled by train to Pier 60 on the North River, New York City, where they boarded the *SS Cedric*, a passenger ship contracted from the White Star Line. Men from the heavy artillery batteries and most others were taken to the Commonwealth Pier in the Charleston Harbor of Boston, there boarding the *HSS Cardiganshire*, a transport owned by Great Britain. These ships joined others in the Halifax Harbor, Bay of Fundy, and 17 vessels headed in convoy across the Atlantic on 1 June.

The procedure for boarding was replicated at each ship; as the men passed up the gang-plank they were handed a numbered ticket, which gave them an assigned place to sleep in the string of hammocks hung throughout the hold, and a place to sit at the mess table. They also were handed a life preserver and assigned a place on a life raft. As the convoy set forth into a slow steady voyage, a new set of rules was vigorously reinforced with notice there would be no absolutions for infractions: no smoking at night, no lights at night, and nothing to be thrown overboard. Censorship was established, with letters home limited to comments on the weather and personal well-being.

Alfonso wrote, "I realize now exactly how it feels to be one of 300 fishing worms in a dark old tomato can; probably smell the same too."

Fire drills and lifeboat practice added to a daily routine of calisthenics, with not much else to do. On 31 May the convoy was met by a flotilla of 10 Allied destroyers that would escort them through the danger zone. Alfonso happened to be on deck in the late afternoon on 2 Jun when the *Arrawa* suddenly jerked hard to starboard. He could see the ship Captain looking through his binoculars with his junior officers shouting and pointing in excitement at the inquisitive periscope of a German submarine that had been spotted about 200 yards astern. Alfonso joined the crew in watching two of the escorting destroyers pirouetting away from the convoy as depth charges tossed high into the air, followed by a shudder felt throughout the ship. Three hundred yards to the rear a huge geyser of black water was followed by a brief glimpse of the bow of the submarine as it lurched up and slid forever more out of sight. Alfonso observed that on 6 Jun dirigibles and airplanes had been added to the surveillance for submarines. He was reassured.

Glorious weather greeted the Brigade as their ship glided into the Mersey River and anchored at one of the mammoth piers of Liverpool, England, on Saturday morning, June 8. The weather stayed kind to the men as they marched 11 miles along cobblestone streets to a British rest camp where they remained for two days. They slept at night on the wooden floor of tents. Alfonso acquired his first cootie, the first of many he would carry in the months to come. The daily menu was:

Breakfast; bread, marmalade, cheese and tea.
Dinner; stewed rabbit, bread, marmalade, cheese and tea.
Supper; a hard-boiled egg, bread, marmalade, cheese and tea.

The country was barren; worn from war. When they had followed their military band through Liverpool, the streets were lined with adoring crowds; Alfonso now could see that much of that cheering was part of a pre-arranged routine. Several times during their march to the rest stop, small crowds would gather with some "glad to see you" remarks mixed with a number of "what took you so long." Most people they encountered simply watched in silence. They looked prematurely aged; grieving widows and soldiers returned with an amputee, all sharing the burden of war.

After a two day rest at the camp, they marched four miles to the railroad station, traveled to Winchester and stayed overnight at a staging area from which they were ferried the next day, 12 June, across the English Channel to LeHavre, France. Alfonso would recall the 10-hour trip as his worst experience of the war, even in the face of the more severe hardships to come. He vomited almost the entire trip, along with most everyone else who was aboard. The savage bouncing and lurching as the boat plunged through an ever-changing tattoo of waves was worse than the combined 11 days crossing the Atlantic Ocean. The experience must have been universal; immediately upon debarking, the men were marched to sulfur baths where they could leave feeling clean for the first time since leaving the States.

Alfonso was surprisingly familiar with the placement of buildings and landmarks of the city as they transversed LeHavre; almost 15 years to the day Alfonso had walked this path in the opposite direction in migration to America. On this day in 1918, the journey from LeHavre was a two-day train ride southwest to Camp Meucon, Vannes, where the Brigade stayed for the next eight weeks and trained with increased intensity. Gazing from the window of the railroad car compartment where he was tightly packed with his battery mates, Alfonso could see women diligently laboring behind plows in the farm fields, driving delivery carts of groceries and meats, handling baggage and manning the trains. Someone in the compartment exclaimed that he had seen a woman shoveling manure onto a wagon and said he knew of no woman in America who would undertake that task. Alfonso explained, "over here wealth is measured by the size of your manure pile." Most of the men thought he was joking.

It was catch-up time for the men most recently assigned to the Regiment, so for Alfonso and others who considered themselves 'seasoned,' the first few weeks was another de ja vu. The circus atmosphere that accompanied the appearance of the occasional airplane or observation balloon, be it friend or foe, was disrupted the day a German pilot dropped a bomb that blew apart the mess. The men of the battery went hungry that day.

About two weeks after their arrival at Camp Meucon, Sergeant Major McGlothan rejoined the 303rd Trench Mortar Battery driving the still fully-equipped Packard truck. Even though the Brigade had been designated as motorized, upon arrival at Camp Meucon the Regiments had been provided with more than 1,000 horses that required stabling and grooming, establishing the transformation to a horse-drawn artillery. The general was able to keep his staff car, the quartermaster held onto his supply trucks, and McGlothan kept the Packard in the same holding area.

"Your real work is just starting," BGen. Hearn announced to his men, "and the most that you can do is the least that is expected of you."

Every effort was made to quickly prepare for active service. All officers and enlisted specialists attended school the entire day; study included the 75mm, gas drills, practice marches and overnight trips with tactical problems such as night occupation of positions. Entraining and detraining came to be another rote activity, as was the routine of bivouacking for the night.

The Trench Mortar Battery practiced at night; wearing gas masks the entire time, they moving into position, assembling and disassembling their 58 mm cannon. The men believed they could place the mortar into service while they were asleep, and they got their chance to demonstrate that belief when McGlothan kept them busy for 48 hours without sleep. Their last night of rehearsal came on a night with a darkened moon creating a black that Alfonso had only previously experienced at the end of a tunnel in a coal mine.

Alfonso joked that he got his first taste of war when he got his first 'cootie bite.' This masked his vision of train loads of wounded and men resting from active service in the front lines. Leave them their peace, McGlothan advised the men of his battery who were anxious to hear first-hand stories about what they were about to face. "You will not understand if they told you," he said, "and if you did understand, you would not ask."

On 20 Aug 1918 the 153rd Field Artillery Brigade began to entrain for the front. Alfonso would begin to understand.

chapter five

The field order that engaged the United States Army in the Great War opened with a clear directive—the First Army will cut off the St. Mihiel salient. The field order set the goal. Planners at General Pershing's newly established First Army headquarters, led by Colonel George C. Marshall, had to figure out how to get the job done while simultaneously positioning 400,000 troops to support the Meuse-Argonne offensive set for early Fall.

The weakest point in the line drawn by the German Armies across France and Belgium in 1914 was the bulge presented at the St. Mihiel salient. The enemy had held the salient against repeated assaults from the French who lost more than 100,000 men in the Bois-le-Pretre. Alfonso soon would get a bird's eye view of the forest, which by 1918 had become a vast open space of stumps, trenches, and debris. Each year the German trench system and wire entanglements had become more elaborate and the enemy dugouts and living quarters more luxurious. The Germans held the salient, 16 miles deep, as protection for the city-fortress of Metz, the Briey coal mines, and the Metz-Sedan lateral railway to Flanders. The terrain in the salient had been rolling country with open hilltops and wooded ravines. Now its outstanding feature was a continuous and complete trench system, including concrete dugouts, that had been under construction for four years and extended approximately seven kilometers (4 ½ mile) in depth.

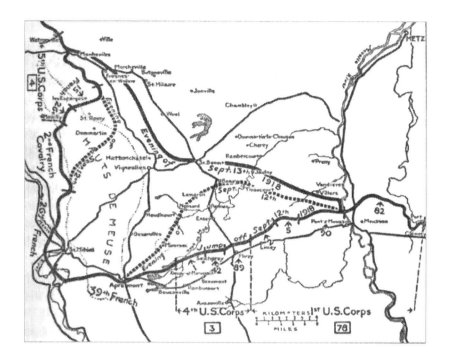

On 24 July, General John J. Pershing met with the commanders of the British and French armies, Field Marshal Douglas Haig
and Field Marshal Philippe Petain, to review plans that had been
prepared at Allied headquarters for pressing the war through the
remainder of 1918. The salient was a part of the front designated as
the American sector; the reduction of the salient would straighten
the line in preparation for a coordinated joint Meuse-Argonne
offensive. A timetable had yet to be set.

To the war planners, this meant use all available units to reduce
the salient and then shift them into line with their assigned divisions in time for the major offensive. For the 153rd Field Artillery
Brigade, this meant boarding the trains that were marked with the
now familiar sign "Hommes 40 Chevaux 8" for a three-day train
ride beginning 20 August. For Alfonso, this meant he was a step
away from the front lines. The Brigade traveled by train almost
directly east from Vannes to Toul, then marched to Martincourt
and staged in an area of the Foret de Puvenelle.

The heat of the late summer day that moved gently with the slight breeze belied the cacophony of activity that began to stir as men with horses and machines prepared to crowd the roadways leading north. It was one of the few breaks from a constant sprinkling of rain that had been with the Brigade since deployment. It was late afternoon of 24 August and Alfonso had just finished reviewing the preparedness checklist on the two Standard B trucks that McGlothan had requisitioned to completely motorize the trench battery. The quartermaster had listed the trucks as Standard B; the men who would ride them into battle would affectionately call them Liberty trucks.

Alfonso stood talking with Pfc. Paul B. Canfield who was completing his own checklist of the Brigade staff car, a Model-T Ford sedan; Canfield served as chauffer for BGen. Clint C. Hearn. The two drivers had been sharing their observations of the civilians in Villers-en-Haye. Alfonso had befriended Canfield due to proximity if nothing else as they often found themselves sharing fellowship at the motor yard. Canfield was from Friendship, New York, a self-described German-Irish monkey wrencher.

After four years of war, the farmers of Villers were seen calmly working their fields as their families had done every day for the generations.

"They seem to recognize the signs of the coming offensive," Canfield observed.

"It would require more than a big offensive to drive those French peasants from their humble homes," Alfonso opined. He had observed that although hostile bombings often drove the family to a cave or cellar, they had become accustomed to such inconveniences.

The men bolted to attention at site of the general who was being following by an entourage that included Sergeant Major McGlothan. Stopping before them, McGlothan said "relax" and with a nod of his head invited them to join in as BGen. Hearn led them on an inspection tour.

The assembly for battle was impressive. They hiked for several miles through a huge area of the Foret de Puvenelle and found it to be alive with the materials of war. There was not a nook or cranny in the woods, behind a ridge, or under the cover of a quarry, that did not conceal a battery, a howitzer, an ammunition dump, a depot of engineering supplies, or a battalion of infantry.

Alfonso would later reflect that the walk down the Tranchée du Milieu and back up the Tranchée de Maidieres, roadways which bisected the dense forest, could be compared to the markets of a county fair with massive displays of materials. Neatly parked and organized were rows of artillery, with acres to the south filled with horses and an acre to the north a parking lot for the motorized vehicles.

The names of the vehicles which were provided through contracts to 294 different manufacturers included Ford, White, FWD, Nash Quad, Packard, Mack, and of course, the Liberty. The trucks came in all shapes, sizes and designs. Rear-view mirrors did not yet exist and windshields were rare. Caterpillar tractors and other tread-driven machines would pull the heavy artillery.

McGlothan explained that the inclusion of motorized transport for the military was still an untried experiment when war broke out in 1914. Back in 1897, General Miles had assigned bicycles to a regiment of troops, with mixed results. The military did not have the funds to pay for untried procedures, so money was raised by private subscription to test long-distance motorized transport. Perhaps sifting for opportunities to profit in the conflict that was engulfing Europe, major contributions were provided by J.P. Morgan, Brown Brothers, Potter, Choate & Prentice, and White, Weld & Company. Fifteen vehicles donated by the manufacturers and more than 1,000 men left the Squadron A Armory on 94th Street and Madison Avenue, New York City, at 10 a.m. Saturday, 7 Aug 1915. McGlothan shared with them a clipping from *The Commercial Vehicle* that provided details:

"The convoy, under the command of Captain Raynal C. Bolling, consisted of one armored car equipped with a machine gun on a swivel mount, two armored motor trucks, three large ammunition transport trucks towing standard U.S. Army limbers and 75mm field guns, one searchlight truck, one ambulance, one officer's car and six miscellaneous vehicles. One of the armored trucks, a Mack, boasted a rapid-firing one-pounder on its body as well as a machine gun. Armor appeared to be on everyone's mind, for one of the heavy transport vehicles, also a Mack, was covered with steel plate to protect the crew and contents. In designing that hefty hauler, the Mack engineers had also placed the radiator—always very susceptible to damage—behind the engine and out of harm's way. The useful load for the truck was 18,000 rounds of .30 caliber machine gun ammunition, 1,800 3-inch shells, plus 500 3-inch shrapnel shells."

The convoy took four days to complete a 400-mile journey, McGlothan concluded, four times as fast as horse-drawn transport and without the burden of having to carry fodder and remounts. He noted that in March of 1916 when General Pershing was ordered to capture the Mexican bandit Pancho Villa by whatever means necessary, Pershing called for five motorized supply trains of 27 vehicles each; at that time the Army had less than 1,000 vehicles in its entire inventory. McGlothan noted that even on the day the United States declared war in 1917, the Army had only 2,400 trucks.

Lessons learned were evident in the organization that prepared the 303rd Trench Mortar Battery to truck into war. Repair shops and spare parts were prepositioned. Keeping vehicles in operation during the Mexican Expedition was a nightmare, McGlothan explained, because 128 different manufacturers had no standardization of parts and the military had few men with mechanical aptitude so civilian mechanics had to be hired. He cast one of his few smiles at Chiappelli when he concluded that the Army now had more than 200,000 vehicles in its pipeline and he knew where to find mechanics.

⸙

GIGANTIC GUNS OF 9.2-INCH CALIBER HAD WADDLED IN DURING the night and by morning were in a neatly camouflaged position at one side of the road, with the crews sound asleep in the mud beside them. German aviators routinely surveyed this area on their dawn patrols and at the first peak of daylight these and all other crews were instructed to stay under cover. At dusk on 25 August the 303rd fell into line behind those guns as they headed north. The trench battery had been tasked with establishing the command post to which headquarters would advance after the attack on the salient began. They were headed to Fey-en-Haye.

In order to keep the date of the advance a secret and surprise the enemy, it was necessary that all traffic move under cover of night. Alfonso would mark this night as one to remember evermore. The caravan of four trucks was led by the White, where McGlothan sat beside the new guy who drove; followed by a Liberty, with Alfonso driving the Packard, followed by the other Liberty. A French officer sat in the truck beside Alfonso; he was serving as an advisor to the field artillery. BGen. Hearn had dumped him off on McGlothan, and McGlothan had placed him in the truck with Chiappelli, suggesting that Alfonso could use his Italian to speak with this Frenchman. There would not be much time for talk.

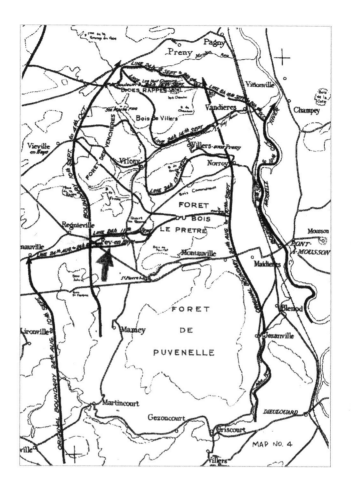

MAP No. 4

The volume of rain increased as the night progressed. The slippery roads were jammed with artillery, trucks, horse transport, automobiles, marching troops, and tractors. Motorcycle messengers bearing important orders picked their precarious way on the edges. No lights were allowed. Alfonso had to follow the muddy, jolty, treacherous roadway using his 'sixth sense' to move beyond an intense awareness born of fear. "The god damna mud," he said to himself, beginning a mantra that would stay with him throughout the war and poke out at points of annoyance through the remainder of his life.

53

All would go well until they ran into a long string of trucks headed in the other direction; then, in the attempt to make the passage, a truck with its heavy load would get stuck in a ditch or spin in place from losing traction in the mud, and all traffic would stop until the machine could resume its place in the parade. Sometimes this was out of the question, and the best that could be done was to push it as far out of the path as possible and abandon it. "The god damna mud."

A source of great trouble was a steep hill with a sharp turn at the top, just upon entering Gezoncourt. They reached this hill within the first hour of their journey. The grade was so pronounced that wheels could not stick to the slippery surface. As the vehicles could not make the ascent under their own power, it was necessary for the men themselves to push the machines through "the god damna mud."

———

THERE WERE TWO TECHNIQUES THAT INSTINCTIVELY WERE adopted by the 303rd wagoneers; the first was to 'close ranks' when climbing a grade, so that if the lead vehicle slowed the others behind could nudge together and use their combined push to get to the top; the second was to link the string of vehicles together with chains so that once over the top, the lead vehicle could help pull the others. These techniques helped at the Gezoncourt grade, but the men still had to get out of the trucks and push. "The god damna mud."

They had many more hills to climb as the Battery headed north. About 0400, the column made a left turn onto the Montauville to Pont-a-Mousson road and headed west to the small farm village of Fey-en-Haye, which proved to be a collection of ruins from about a dozen structures, all surrounded by a sea of god damna mud.

Alfonso was exhausted, both mentally and physically. The constant attention to every detail—an eye on the water gauge and an ear on the idle to keep the radiator from boiling over, a feel for any slip in the wheels, a nose on the brakes to avoid burning them away. The sensations were so alive that Alfonso believed he could even taste the clay and could anticipate the approach to the spot where a likely slide would await in the twists and turns of the roadway. He could appreciate why the artillery men he had observed the morning before had slept in the mud. As soon as he got the signal from Sergeant Major McGlothan that they had reached their destination, Alfonso crawled under his truck and went to sleep. He quickly was joined by the Frenchman and others from the battery, each who fell to their own version of deep slumber.

From the deep recesses of his sleep, Alfonso could hear the desperate orders shouted in sharp command to move no further and the pleading cries of the Frenchman proclaiming he was a friend. Alfonso jolted awake, rolled to a stand, and stepped cautiously around the corner of the bombed out building where they had parked, just in time to see several soldiers armed with rifles running up behind an American officer who was pointing a pistol at the Frenchman whose pants hung to his knees while his arms were raised above his head.

The Frenchman had the urge to urinate and the courtesy to step beyond his bunkmates. Turns out that the 303rd Trench Mortar Battery had moved into line in front of the infantry division assigned to secure that area. The Mountauville to Pont-a-Mousson road drew the east-to-west line that marked the border to the Bois-le-Pretre. They had moved in front of the front line.

chapter six

Bois-le-Pretre was the forest which had been the scene of desperate fighting between the French and Germans in 1915. The action which occurred there was typical of the bitter trench fighting which characterized the World War. The trenches of the opposing forces were so close together that an ordinary tone of voice in the German trenches would be audible to the French. The struggle never ceased, and the harassing by artillery, hand grenades, machine guns, and raiding parties continued day and night. A gain of a few yards was sometimes warranted of sufficient importance to receive notice in the official communiqué. As the sector quieted down, the Germans and French drew further apart, leaving No Man's Land, a reach of just over half a mile. What had once been a dense forest was reduced to nothing more than a waste of stumps; the scene was repeated through the front lines.

At the time the 90th division entered the sector, this No Man's Land was of an average width of one kilometer (just over 1/2 mile), and was filled with the maze of trenches and wire which was once a part of the front-line systems. The ruins of the village Fey-en-Haye were left unoccupied between the contending forces, until sometime in that early morning hour before dawn on 26 August 1918 when in moved the 303rd Trench Mortar Battery.

The 303rd had much to prepare. Information obtained from German prisoners and other intelligence supported the conclusion that the enemy was stockpiling Yellow Cross shells opposite their sector; this meant mustard gas. McGlothan was given instructions to construct a gas-proof dugout "where the men could rest in safety without the discomfort and fatigue that will come from wearing their respirators." Chloride of lime was in short supply, so McGlothan arranged instead a series of wash stands through which men could use quantities of soap suds to clean the mustard gas from their eyes, nose, and throat in the event of contamination.

Alfonso spent most of his days sleeping or providing maintenance and small repairs to the Packard truck. During the nights he drove to a train depot near Pont-a-Mousson in a sector held by the 82nd Division and moved materials to ammunition dumps prepositioned for the 153rd Regiments which were queuing up to move into the line. Other men of the battery were engaged in cleaning out the old French trenches in No Man's Land from which the 90th Division infantry would launch the attack. During three years of inactivity, the trenches had become filled with wire and trash. All the work had to be done silently, under cover of darkness, and the trash had to be disposed of out of sight. The rolling artillery barrage that the men of the 90th would follow into battle would fall 500 meters to their front; mistakes in preparation would cost lives.

Their mission ostensibly was to cut wire, and they were more successful than on any other part of the front, but not due to their shelling. The first two weeks were quiet ones. Batteries were not permitted to fire. The mission for the time being was a defensive one and it was important not to disclose the strength of the forces assembling for the coming attack of the First Army. On one of his trips to Pont-a-Mousson, following instructions from McGlothan, Alfonso loaded his truck with as many wire cutters as he could requisition.

⁂

THE DRIVE TO THE TRAIN DEPOT WAS NERVE RACKING, BUT ALFONSO was far less anxious about this reoccurring nighttime adventure than he had been on the trip from Martincourt. He marveled at the massing of troops, artillery, trucks and supply trains. During the nights all roads were alive with activity and jammed beyond their capacity, but when daylight came scarcely a man or vehicle of any kind could be seen. The troops were carefully hidden in the thick woods and trucks, cannon and horses were carefully screened by boughs or hidden in the edges of woods. As soon as it was dark again, every road came alive.

He chuckled to himself when recalling an introductory lecture from his first days in the Army at Camp Lee. An officer admonished that men in the artillery were not real soldiers because they would be excused from the face-to-face fighting that the infantry would experience. Alfonso would concede that while part of that sentiment was true, he stood equally in harm's way. The gas mask had become a natural extension of his face.

The divisional Summaries of Intelligence for the three weeks prior to 12 September record the number of enemy shells falling in the sector on 14 of those 21 days. Gas shells as well as HE (high explosive) fell on 11 of the 14 days, for a cumulative total of 5,639 rounds, including approximately 700 gas rounds, almost all blue and green cross shell. As certainty of the attack grew, enemy harassing fire increased gradually over the three-week period, from as few as 60 rounds on 24 August to as many as 1,000 rounds on 9 September. The greatest number of gas shells reported on any one day was 200, recorded on 4 September, resulting in 14 casualties.

This is just a small part of a much larger puzzle, Alfonso reflected, as slow and steady he moved his truck with the traffic. His analytical skills had advanced considerably since his transfer to the 303rd, pressed to think forward by McGlothan while also learning to place that thinking in context with the larger mission. Reminded him of a favorite passage that he had memorized a long time ago:

> "To be constantly aware of the great whole in which you exist is to cultivate stability and a sense of proportion. The unhappy person, the over-busy person, lives in the narrow cell of his own obsessions. The person who can laugh at his troubles is the person who, knowing that he is the center of his universe, knows also that his ego is not the whole universe. He is in contact with his whole environment, not just a part of it."

There were only a few officers in American Expeditionary Force with experience in handling large-scale operations and commander-in-chief General Pershing, needed every one of them on his staff. He took it upon himself to command the First Army. He summarized the needs at his first staff meeting in ordering the Army into motion:

> "There must be railroads and lines of communication and depots of supplies of all sorts and experienced officers who know how to get those supplies forward to the fighting organizations. Then there is the aviation service, the tank corps, the long guns of the artillery, the special gas and smoke troops, telephone battalions, the increased medical personnel and hospitals and supplies, engineers to rebuild the roads and railroads as the advance progresses not to mention the hundreds of military police required for the control of traffic and the evacuation of prisoners, and the salvage squads to reclaim and save the debris of battle."

Army Field Order 9 presented the plan of attack. Four Army Corps, three American and one French, would advance on Hatton-ville-Vigneulles in a pincers movement to cut off the enemy forces in the salient. In an operation expected to take two to three days, 5th Corps was to swing in from the west, with 4th Corps swinging in from the south like two large gates closing in a corral. The 1st Corps, which included the 90th Division, would anchor the hinge at the Moselle River, secure the flank, and support the clockwise movement of the 4th Corps arm. The 2nd French Corps would advance an hour later than the other Corps, pushing through the center in a mop-up action. Placed in line to accomplish this mission were 216,000 American and 48,000 French troops, with 100,000 American troops held in reserve. Support would come from the more than 3,000 cannons, 400 tanks and 1,480 airplanes committed to the fight.

The 1st Army Corps, commanded by Major General Hunter Liggett, was composed of five divisions. Three divisions were to attack: the 90th on the right, the 5th in the center, and the 2nd on the left. The 82nd Division, which straddled the Moselle River, was to hold in place at this important connection to the supply line. The 78th Division was in reserve, although its artillery Brigade which included Alfonso and the trench battery already stood in the front lines. The 153rd Brigade would fight with the 90th Division. The divisional plan of attack was set forth in Field Order No. 3, issued at 1700 hours (5 p.m.) 9 September, which prescribed that the brigades would fight side by side, and that in each brigade the regiments would be placed side by side. Since the Division was the pivot for the entire offensive, it was provided that the 180th Brigade, in the right sub-sector, should merely hold on part of its front and make a limited advance on the remainder of its front, while to the 179th Brigade fell the task of pushing ahead on the left, keeping in step with men from the 4th Corps, requiring an advance of four kilo-meters (2 ½ miles). The width of the divisional front was about six kilometers (3 ¾ miles).

There was to be no artillery preparation in advance of the attack. The troops were to advance under a massive rolling barrage, with the artillery action set to start on D Day at H Hour. The mortar battery was to be provided with phosphorus bombs, to be used for smoke screens as desired, and with thermite for use against machine-gun nests or other enemy units within their range.

BGen. Hearn went berserk with rage, according to his driver Canfield.

Hearn was clearly disturbed by the absence of preparatory fire. In addition to the 18 batteries of organic guns and mortars in the 153rd Brigade, he noted in his initial operations order, that he would be reinforced by 15 batteries of French artillery. Hearn also had 2 batteries of 58mm trench mortar. Hearn said: "It is believed that a few hours of artillery action on the Bois-le-Pretre will reduce that stronghold to a state affording an easy, although necessarily slow, advance."

When he reported to division headquarters on 28 August, Hearn had immediately gone to work to convince the higher-ups that they should let him do his job. Consequently the word had gone out to his Regiment commanders in a series of countermanding orders. The artillery preparation was at first to be 4 ½ hours, then 14 hours, then 22 hours, then no artillery preparation, and finally 4 hours.

No hours of preparation were specified on 1 September when the Ordnance Officer for the First Army directed that a 5-day allowance of ammunition be on hand for the attack, with 75mm in proportion of 65 percent HE (high explosive), 15 percent shrapnel, and 20 percent gas and smoke; 155mm in proportion of 90 percent HE, 10 percent gas, the gas to be 50 percent each of the #4 and #5 (cyanogen and phosgene).

That same day at headquarters, the French planners were insisting that a long artillery preparation precludes any possibility of a surprise attack, and surprise was an essential element to this operation. Field Marshal Petain went even further. He demanded that Pershing abandon all planning, turn his Divisions over to the

French and British for deployment on other fronts, and have the American First Army serve as a decoy to pull German troops to the salient by providing little more than a demonstration.

"Do you wish to take part in this battle?" the French commander asked with a combination of arrogance and dismissiveness, insinuating that the American army was not ready to go into battle on its own. General Pershing shouted, "as an American army and in no other way," according to Pfc. Canfield who sat rigidly at the steering wheel of the Ford staff car with the flag officers huddled in conference on the back seat.

Our Blackjack told him straight out, Canfield reported, that no American soldier would ever report to any other than an American officer. And Pershing told him we would be in position by the 26th of September to handle our part of the Meuse-Argonne offensive.

"Will we be ready by then?" Alfonso had asked. "A bear's chance in hell," Canfield had quipped in a noncommittal response.

Canfield previously had reported the substance of this conversation to BGen. Hearn who had stated with an assuring confidence as if it already were an established fact: "close the salient and launch a major offensive in two weeks," adding the Army worn cliché "finish the job and get home by Christmas."

The concerns Hearn had voiced regarding lack of artillery preparation had reached the ears of MGen. Liggett. Liggett was a thinking man's officer, who had served as president of the Army War College where then-Captain Hearn had lectured on the use of artillery. Liggett was 40 pounds overweight and routinely countered criticism from colleagues by saying "there is nothing wrong with fat, so long as it is not above the collar."

As in all matters of military politics, General Liggett asked that the issues be put forth in writing. His staff officers had objected to the French advisors crowding headquarters with the continued insistence, "be reasonable, do it our way." Do not want to do it the French way, Liggett thought to himself; their top down directives had drained their reservoir of men. They would fight the American way. Decisions needed to be made at the point where information met command.

The argument for preparation before H hour was summarized in a document written by Lt. Colonel W.S. Grant and Colonel George C. Marshall. Even if the plans are not executed, they argued, each Regiment should be prepared to provide preparation support so that if any last minute intelligence should deem the support necessary the commanders on scene could make an informed decision. They offered nine reasons why an artillery preparation should precede an assault:

- There was no instance in the war where an attack had been made against a highly organized position without an adequate artillery preparation.

- To attack without preparation was taking a gambler's chance.

- The preparation could do no harm and might make the operation easier by shaking the enemy's morale; it would cause breaches in the enemy's trenches and wire, put confidence in our troops, and put hostile batteries out of action.

- A preparation would permit a certain amount of registration.

- The preparation would serve as interdiction fire against enemy reinforcements and keep the enemy from altering his dispositions.

- To omit the preparation would deprive Army of a powerful weapon.

- The preparation would take the place of large tanks, which were not available, for cutting the enemy wire. There were not enough medium and small tanks on hand for the job.

- The argument that preparation should start at daylight to keep the location of batteries in the open concealed from the enemy was not valid. Army's superiority was too great for enemy batteries to interfere, and the batteries could be put in reasonably concealed localities for the preparation.

* Many areas such as woods, etc., should be drenched with gas before our troops are to pass through them, the gas bombardment on these places ceasing several hours before our troops arrive there. If there is no artillery preparation until H Hour we will be deprived of the use of gas on those localities where the necessity of gas is the greatest.

On 7 September the order for attack read: "The artillery fire (including preparation) will start at H Hour minus the time desired by corps commanders for beginning of the barrage fire. If gas is used it will cease four hours before the attack."

Beginning the night of 9 September the 153rd Field Artillery Brigade under the command of Brigadier General Clint C. Hearn moved by echelon into position. As they were moving into position, several batteries belonging to the 308th Field Artillery Regiment were sighted by a German observation balloon and severely shelled, losing several men, a number of horses, and one 75mm howitzer. The location of part of the 309th Regiment was discovered by the Germans almost at once and their positions were severely shelled, adding to the casualty list.

The Brigade had been tasked to support the 90th Division, men from Texas and Oklahoma who had trained for this moment for more than a year but had yet to taste battle. The right boundary of the sector assigned to the 90th Division was about two kilometers (1 ¼ mile) west of the Moselle River, with the front line the border to the Bois-le-Pretre beginning at a point about three kilometers (2 miles) northwest of Pont-e-Mousson and extending west just over nine kilometers (5 ½ miles) to a point just south of Remenauville, another bombed-out farm village with this one held by the Germans.

The two battalions of the 307th Field Artillery took up positions under cover of road embankments and patches of woods in the neighborhood of Auberge-St. Pierre. The 308th Field Artillery was placed in the woods west of Montauville on both sides of the highway. The battalions of 155's composing the 309th Field Artillery Regiment were along the northern edge of the Foret de Puvenelle. At 1630 (4:30 p.m.) on 11 September, with eight hours to go, BGen. Hearn delivered the final plans: "Gas shell will be fired by heavy artillery on targets occupied by enemy personnel toward the rear of the zone of advance. The six battalions of 75mm that have been assigned the mission of creeping and protective barrage will fire gas shell from H minus 4 hours to H minus 2 hours on targets occupied by enemy personnel. From H minus 2 to H Hour, these same battalions and heavy artillery will fire on the first and second lines of enemy wire. The allowance for the operation will be two day's fire. As much of the gas shell as possible will be fired in order to leave high explosives for the later phases of the attack."

The night of 11 September was black as ink and the rain was coming down in sheets. The artillery opened fire at 0100 (1 a.m.) and for two hours all batteries fired nonpersistent gas into occupied areas in the Bois-le-Pretre and the rear of the main zone of advance. The 303rd trench mortars were applied as prescribed; targets were selective, mostly machine gun nests. The final count for the 12 September action: the 153rd Field Artillery Brigade fired 49,400 75mm shells, including 1,100 gas rounds; 8,500 155mm shells, including 500 gas rounds; and 6,200 rounds fired from the trench batteries.

In order to conceal the fact of the changed positions from the enemy, no fire for adjustment had been permitted and the firing data for some batteries arrived at the battalion command posts as late as 2200 hours (10 p.m.) on the night of the 11 Sep. After firing the preliminary bombardment, the Brigade put down its first rolling barrage at 0500 hours in the morning, protecting the vigorous advance made by the 90th Division infantry. This rolling barrage was afterwards the subject of general praise and comment by the infantry, who stated that it was clock-like in its precision and that they had no difficulty in advancing under it.

The intense training and travel through the war-worn country had prepared Alfonso for this moment. He had grown accustomed to the sight, to the obnoxious smells, could feel the lice, and taste the ever-present god damn mud. But nothing had prepared him for the noise. Certainly they had fired their artillery in practice. Alfonso would compare the experience to that of a musical instrument that you learn to play in the seclusion of a room now being added to the complete orchestra. The noise was loud, and continuous.

The artillery preparation had barely begun when word reached the command post that some of the batteries were not firing their gas shells. BGen. Hearn had added this concern to his earlier list of worries. He had heard through the grapevine that some of the officers in command of his artillery batteries had been discussing the ethics of using gas as a wartime weapon. This is neither the time nor place for this debate Hearn told his Regiment commanders; he put them on notice that they would be held personally responsible for any hesitation in complying with orders. Hearn was not buying the explanation that the gas shells could not be distinguished from the other shells because it was too dark.

McGlothan immediately was granted a field promotion and ordered to take command of the 307th Regiment; the commander who was relieved was placed in charge of one of the batteries that had yet to fire its gas shells and the officer who had been directing that battery was sent to the rear echelon to face charges in the after-math. At 0500 (5 a.m.) on 12 September, as the artillery preparation was ending, the rain began to let up.

In addition to the truckload of wire cutters that Alfonso had transported to Fey-en-Haye, the men of the 90th Division had 400 pairs of French heavy duty, two-handed wire cutters they had purchased in shops enroute to the front. Using the wire cutters, the men from Texas and Oklahoma were able to cut a path through the wire as fast as a wave of infantry could walk, stopped only for short periods of time by entanglements. They were part of the 23-kilo-meter (14 mile) arm that extended as the southern gate; that gate closed ahead of schedule as the American First Army reclaimed the St. Mihiel salient.

The advance of the 90th infantry was a bit slow in the center, clogged as it was by the previous wages of war. The charge along the bordering ridges progressed more rapidly, providing a flanking on both sides of the German held territory in the Bois-le-Pretre, forcing the enemy to withdraw. Alfonso had been heavily engaged in support of the trench mortars; connected via telephone thanks to the communications troops, the mortar batteries received an ongoing stream of coordinates to place their shell in identified targets. With the speed of their advance, the 90th infantry moved beyond the range where the trench mortars could offer support. The assigned duty for the trench battery now was to provide a defensive ring around the command post. The command staff had moved forward with the advance and headquarters now was located at Fey-en-Haye. The next day McGlothan led his artillery regiment to forward positions that helped secure the gate that the American Army had closed on the St. Mihiel salient.

By early morning on the 13th of September, observers reported that the enemy was out of range for the light regiments and it was found that even by depressing the trails and using maximum elevation the enemy could not be reached. New positions were at once selected and between the 14th and 16th of September, the entire brigade had moved up in front of the Bois-le-Pretre, facing Pagny-sur-Moselle. From then until the time the brigade left the sector, there was plenty of opportunity to practice all the artillery principles learned in training camps. The next three weeks were spent organizing the new front inside what had been the powerful Saint Mihiel Salient.

The 90th Division felt the brunt of German retaliatory action that was administered the next day. Maintaining their assigned position at the hinge, the men moved forward only a few kilometers if at all; known coordinates for the enemy gunners. Beginning at 0600 in the morning of 13 September and lasting until 1500 in the afternoon, between 600 and 750 blue cross (diphenylchlorarsine) and green cross (diphosgene) shells had fallen along the division front between Fey-en-Haye to Pont-a-Mousson. There were 104 casualties in the four regiments as the troops, numbed by rain and cold, failed to adjust their masks in time or remained in gas concentrations in the shell holes and removed their masks too soon. More damaging was the toll the shelling took on the horses who had no respiratory protection.

Under gas bombardment, some of the artillery gunners wore the mouthpiece and nose clip, but would not don the mask properly because of fogging of eye pieces. Consistently they took their masks off too soon because they did not detect a smell. The woods were full of odors from dead animals, crushed foliage, upturned earth, rotten wood, HE, and gas. In trying to hold the salient, the Germans used little or no gas in the other sectors. More than a third of the battle casualties in the 90th Division came from gas assaults, with more than 1,500 men taking home permanent lung damage or blindness.

BGen. Hearn was a strong advocate on the use of gas; he was willing to fire all the gas shell he could get. His numerous instruction memoranda on the moving of crews and guns under gas attack, the handling of leaking gas shell, and the degree of gas discipline required of artillerymen were provided to assure his men that he understood their wariness concerning gas shell. Hearn insisted that with proper handling, firing gas shell was no more hazardous than HE. Hearn also wanted retaliation for the men he had lost in battle. Added to the loss of men from the 308th who had been caught in the open, were casualties from the 309th which had been targeted by enemy gunners on day one of the attack. He thirsted for retaliation.

The fact that the Germans were daily firing three or four gas shells to each one fired by the 153rd made valid the repeated complaint by BGen. Hearn that he could not get enough ammunition. Retaliation served to raise the spirits of the division, he maintained in writing, "The dread of enemy gas is so profound that the knowledge that we are using gas on the Boche increases the morale of our officers and men and causes general satisfaction throughout the division. It is suggested that an endeavor be made to provide each battery at the close of action with a plentiful supply of gas and that as soon as observation is obtained a plan of retaliation fire be put into effect. It is believed that a severe program of retaliation with high explosive and gas will assist materially in reducing the enemy's fire during the period of consolidation."

In his after-action report, Captain McGlothan wrote: "An occasional shell or volley dropped with accuracy will accomplish much more than a world of ammunition fired merely upon map data."

Continuing the program of retaliation, on 27 to 28 September the 153rd artillery fired 113 rounds of phosgene (#5) gas and 240 rounds of mixed #5 and HE on enemy batteries in the town of Preny. On the afternoon of 29 September, 32 rounds of #5 were fired into the Pagny railroad yards. Continuing into the next day, a total of 103 rounds of phosgene, 125 rounds of yperite, and 40 cyanogen gas rounds were fired on batteries and camps in the Preny-Pagny area. The day after that, 52 rounds of phosgene and yperite and 40 other gas rounds were fired at crossroads, and 32 rounds were placed in the Pagny yards.

BGen. Hearn said, "The purpose of this fire is to kill Boche in retaliation for the casualties he is causing us. In order to get maximum results this fire must be short, accurate, and from all guns simultaneously. As soon as one shot falls the enemy will take cover, therefore the uselessness of continued firing. However, just to greet him when he comes out again, gas will habitually be mixed with high explosive in this firing.

Through the night of 2 October, 37 rounds of yperite and 56 other gas rounds were fired with HE on enemy crossroads and shelters and 100 large-caliber yperite shells and 135 additional gas rounds were put on Preny. On the 3rd and 4th of October, in its last fire missions in support of the 90th, the 153rd FA Brigade fired 66 round of yperite, phosgene, and cyanogen on those same enemy targets.

The 153rd Brigade then withdrew and rejoined the 78th Division as it moved west to take position in line with the Meuse-Argonne offensive that had been launched on 26 September.

In the aftermath and in his defense on failure to launch gas shells, the officer who was charged with dereliction of duty presented this argument: "The failure to use gas shell was due to lack of appreciation of its tactical advantages during an offensive operation; uncertainty on the length of the artillery preparation; impossibility of using gas extensively prior to the artillery preparation, to preserve secrecy; adverse weather conditions; and over-sensitiveness to the risks involved to our own troops." Due to the adverse weather conditions—driving rain had persisted throughout the early morning hours—the officer was excused from any further response to the charges.

chapter seven

Alfonso had been with his unit in front-line action for more than a month; they had become battle-hardened and weary, maintaining constant alert to a job that continued 24 hours daily and was a long way from done. In the days after the advance, he and battery mates were detailed to the 303rd engineers to help rebuild roads that had been washed away with the rains or blasted away by enemy shells. Always leave them better than you found them, Alfonso remembered the repeated advice as they inspected and repaired every crossing and every bridge.

Alfonso was not prepared for the chaotic traffic jams on the roads when he accelerated the Packard into traffic on "The Road." The 7th of October was another foggy, drizzly day. The god damn mud; even Captain McGlothan was repeating the ever present observation. A new commander had been assigned to the 307th Field Artillery Regiment and McGlothan was back with the 303rd Trench Mortar Battery, which now traveled with the headquarters staff as the 153rd Field Artillery Brigade shifted 60 miles to its new assignment. The Brigade was headed to Apremont where it would bivouac and provision for its next role.

The Trench Mortar Battery pulled into one of the eight repair stations that had been positioned on a road that was dubbed the *Voie Sacree*—the Sacred Way led to the Verdun, the front of the Meuse-Argonne offensive. After the war the Voie Sacree was designated a National Road and has since been maintained by France as a military monument.

In 1916 the road was just a small, narrow, locally-maintained, two-lane trail, 75 kilometers (46 miles) long and 7 meters (22 feet) wide. A small army of laborers, mostly old or disabled soldiers, threw 700,000 tons of crushed stone over the road in a 10-month period to establish a stable supply route. The local civilians who lived along the route stepped from their homes and joined the soldiers in not only building the road, but in many cases providing daily maintenance on the footage that stepped along their property lines. Quarries were opened nearby to feed The Road a steady diet of crushed stone.

Alfonso had learned from the 303rd engineers that a special unit of 8,000 drivers and mechanics and 300 officers had been tasked with controlling traffic and servicing vehicles. The Voie Sacree had been closed to all horse-drawn and foot traffic; its use was restricted to the 3,000 French trucks in service, mostly Berliet but also trucks from the Renault, Latil and Schneider plants—all with solid rubber tires—and 800 Ford Model T ambulances run by the American Ambulance Service. Prepositioned along the Voie Sacree were 30 repair trucks and eight mobile tire replacement shops with hydraulic presses.

The trucks had moved mostly artillery ammunition, as was happening now, with 75mm brass-cased shells pre-packaged in wooden crates, while the155mm shells were shipped unboxed and separate from their powder charges. The traffic never stopped on the Voie Sacree, moving day and night at a consistent 15 miles per hour; breakdowns resulted in vehicles being pushed off the road to an area that would not interrupt the flow of traffic. During its peak, 6000 trucks made the trek in a single day, equating to 250 trucks an hour or 1 truck every 14 seconds.

Alfonso was disgusted to learn that on this day the Voie Sacree was crammed with soldiers fleeing from the front. His disgust was compounded by the influenza that he had contracted and of course, the god damna mud which had turned the roads into gumbo. The flu was rampant throughout the Brigade, with deaths from the disease beginning to match the number of men lost from battle.

The motorized 303rd Trench Mortar Battery and other motor transport left at 1900 hours on 5 October and staged overnight at Saulx, rested at Rumont on the 6th, and reached its destination at Camp Chillaz on the 7th of October.

The horse-drawn Artillery Brigade and Ammunition Train moved from the Puvenelle sector by way of a village trail connecting Regnieville-Euvezin-Pannes-Nonsard and then into the Bois de la Belle Oziere and Bois d'Euvezin for cover. The brigade had never had its full complement of animals and had lost many from sickness while in the line. Consequently the work of moving the guns and caissons was doubly hard upon the remaining beasts and both animals and men were badly in need of a rest when they reached the Futeau region west of the area in which the infantry were camped.

Alfonso later learned from Canfield all the details of what had been happening with the major offensive that had been launched on 26 September while the 153rd was busy with its work in the salient.

It was mid-morning on 15 October and Canfield had won a hard earned break; BGen. Hearn rarely stopped moving from one meeting to another. The decision had been made; the now united 78th Division and artillery would move to the front. Verbal orders had been delivered with detailed discussion on the tactics that would need to be applied and the larger strategy that those tactics would fit into. This standard-issue hurry up and wait moment was provided by the usual directive: be prepared to move out the moment instructions are received in writing.

After they had settled in for the respite at Apremont, BGen. Hearn had continued on to the headquarters of now-Lieutenant General Liggett who had been given command of the First Army. Canfield heard details of lessons learned as BGen. Hearn used his return-trip time in the staff car to prepare orders that would move the 153rd Field Artillery to the forefront of plans for a renewed attack. Canfield had his ear stuck as rigid as a fly on flypaper.

Hearn was pleased to note that before the 250,000 soldiers ordered forward by General Pershing at dawn on 26 September to launch the

Meuse-Argonne offensive, an all-night barrage was provided by 3,928 artillery cannon, adding gun smoke to the fog that drifted into the ravines. Of the nine divisions that surged forward, only four divisions had men who had experienced earlier combat action; two of the divisions were recent arrivals to Europe and were new to the lines. They were expected to advance 10 miles up the valley, clearing the enemy from the Argonne forest by bursting through the German defense.

The primeval glacier that had originally gouged out the valley had left behind a hogback running down the middle of the Argonne, with ridges slanting off at odd angles, effectively dividing the Argonne into two tunnel-like defiles. General Liggett called it a natural fortress. Inside the Argonne were ravines, hillocks and meandering little streams that added to obstacles created by fallen trees and dense undergrowth that reduced visibility to 20 feet.

Throughout the valley, the Germans were prepared—parallel and flanking trenches, concrete dugouts, sniper nests armed with machine guns and surrounded by camouflage and barbed wire, with dozens of heavy artillery positioned on the high ground. While the foot soldiers might have been encouraged by the presence of 400 tanks, including a brigade led by Colonel George C. Patton, that morale boost was short lived; before the first day ended, two-thirds of the tanks were disabled. Tanks broke down in the brutal terrain and the Germans had learned to use a 77mm field piece to blast the tanks apart at point-blank range.

As they pressed their attack, the 35th Division literally fell apart. These men from National Guard units drawn from Kansas and Missouri had severe command problems going into battle; on the eve of the attack several infantry commanders were replaced with veterans. By day three of the attack the Division had lost all cohesiveness, with men wandering off in every direction, sometimes together, often alone and lost. One of the few units in the Division to stay intact was an artillery battery commanded by Capt. Harry S. Truman.

"I could never see that happening in the 90th," Alfonso interrupted. "Those boys knew how to work together. You shoulda seen them. No panic. No running. Movin forward lika they justa stroll through the cattle pen."

"Your English is improving," Canfield teased. He continued to fill in the news that happened during their time in action at the salient.

By 1 October the Meuse-Argonne offensive had ground to a halt. Pershing visited each Division, screamed and yelled, replaced commanders, and finally replaced Divisions, withdrawing three green Divisions from the center and replacing those men with veterans. The offensive was renewed on 4 October with a somewhat similar result. A Division of New York men became the "Lost Battalion" when 540 men were cut off in the Ravin de Chaulevaux. The men stuck together and were reunited with their brethren thanks to an intelligent maneuver directed by General Liggett.

The 82nd Division was ordered into the line on 10 October. After replacing the previously assigned units, the men of the 82nd abandoned the front lines and attacked laterally into the flank of the Germans who had entrapped the New Yorkers. These were the 82nd men from Tennessee whom Alfonso had befriended on his many trips to Pont-a-Mousson. Among their number was Corporal Alvin York, who single-handedly captured 132 enemy prisoners.

Alfonso learned that the traffic jam on the Voie Sacree that he had so bemoaned was caused by more than 100,000 stragglers who were wandering around the rear area. General Pershing had cannibalized seven Divisions of troops recently arriving in France, including some men who had been in uniform for only a few months, and had sent the unseasoned troops to the front line as replacements. Canfield noted that it was on that very morning on the 10th of October that General Pershing had issued an order that deserters were to be shot at the immediate discretion of the Regiment commanders.

That was the same day, 10 October, that General Pershing turned command of the First Army over to General Liggett. Liggett immediately announced that it was time to rest and regroup. While rounding up the 100,000 stragglers and returning them to their units and restoring order in the rear, Liggett set to work to reform the First Army. He issued orders to stop charging machine guns and strongpoints that were holding up an advance. Regiments and divisions no longer were to consider boundary lines as no-trespass signs. They should assist their neighbors with flank attacks and decide at the battle site how to progress. 10 October also was the day the 153rd Field Artillery Brigade rejoined the 78th Division, the first time the units had been together since arriving in France.

"I know those guys," Alfonso exclaimed, remembering the Tennessee men of the 82nd Division. "They sure are a scrawny bunch. Did nota look lika soldiers, but this mountain land must be lika their home."

"Have you noticed the one thing we all have in common is that we have nothing in common?" Canfield asked.

"Sure, and nonna us wantsa to be here," Alfonso added.

"The most you have to do is the least that is expected of you," Canfield retorted. The men took every opportunity to quote BGen. Hearn. "What are you going to do when you get back home, you know, after the war?" The question was unexpected because it was personal.

Alfonso responded slowly, "work on cars; probably go back in mines for a while," hesitated and asked, "why you ask?"

"Just talking my thoughts out loud," Canfield said. "I've been thinking about all the chances we'll have to make money on the things we've seen here. Stuff like how well the repair shops are organized and standardized, and the mobile tow trucks to keep them connected. I can see us keeping a fleet of trucks hauling freight."

"You wanna drive trucks?" Alfonso asked.

"What?" Canfield expressed as a question, "you think I want to be a chauffeur all my life? No. What I have in mind is a business proposition. You and I get together with some other dudes we trust, pool our money, and buy up a whole bunch of trucks. You heard McGlothan; 200,000 in the pipeline. After this is all said and done, we can get them cheap. Then we pool our skills together and build a freight system."

"You trust me?" Alfonso replied with surprise. "You hardly know me."

"Trust you the same as anyone else," Canfield offered. "You know what we have in common. Seen what you can do with a truck. Watched you listen to the engine, put your hands on the hood, and know exactly what adjustments to make before you opened her up. You got the touch."

About noon on 15 October, written orders arrived from First Army Corp Headquarters directing the 78th Division to relieve the 77th Division the next night. General Liggett implored the 'Lightning' Division to step forward aggressively and press the enemy's right flank around the town of Grandpre, which sat on a bluff north of the Aire River. For 10 days and 10 nights the 78th attacked, and attacked again, taking heavy casualties in Grandpre and the nearby Bois-de-Loges. Liggett had hoped to convince the Germans that the American's next offensive push would come from the left, with reserves shifted from the center to meet that threat.

Alfonso Chiappelli was to play a key role in this tactical action. He had every reason to kill Germans.

As he and Canfield sat talking, Alfonso could hear the distant drone of an airplane. He did not give the sound much awareness as the Battery was staged not far from an airfield that helped protect the Voie Sacree which often had been the target of German attacks. To dissuade the enemy and protect the highway, airplane squadrons including the Escadrille Americaine were based nearby.

The whizzing bang caught his attention moments before Alfonso was buried in a rain of earth that had sprouted skyward from the exploding shell. He had been thrown sideways into a ditch.

Canfield had not been as lucky. Alfonso shook his head clear of the debris and upon raising his head above the edge of the ditch he could see Canfield being placed upon a stretcher. He followed the stretcher and its bearers to a first aid station where he was told there was no hope; Canfield had been struck squarely in the heart by a tiny piece of shell and had died instantly. The next day Alfonso helped dig a grave for his friend Canfield, whose body wrapped in a blanket was lowered into French soil while a German plane circled overhead.

Alfonso started his Packard, fought with himself until he could control his emotions, and purposefully drove with a determination engaged and an attitude altered.

chapter eight

God damn mud.

The most noticeable change in Alfonso was the almost immediate loss of his Italian accent. When he spoke his mantra the words came out chopped firm and served hard.

The roads were few and bad. The western part of this front in and along the Argonne Forest was the worst; this was one of the wildest regions of France, densely forested, with deep ravines. The roads were nothing more than woodland trails. The Germans had the advantage of high ground and excellent cover.

Alfonso saw at his first glance of the battlefield the work that he would be called upon to do. The 78th would need to charge en masse to secure a foothold. From that point on the fighting would be localized to small groups who would fight for a piece of real estate until they merged with another group; the band then would help neighboring brethren on the flanks, and with this continued combination of forward and flanking actions the men would be able to push together as one. The job of the 303rd was to stay at the center of the action, targeting machine guns and sniper nests. Other units of the artillery were called upon to saturate the field in front to prepare for the next shove.

The 77th had been operating in the Grandpre-St. Juvin sector on a front of three and one-half miles. The relief was ordered to be completed by 1800 hours on 16 October.

There were two chief enemy strongholds against which operations in this sector must be directed—the Bois-des-Loges and the town of Grandpre.

The Bois-des-Loges was a tract of scrub underbrush, a little less than a mile square, cut by many wood trails in all directions and by natural gullies running generally east and west. The woods rose abruptly from the south to a bald peak in the northwest, affording complete observation of the ground in front where the 78th was dug in. French maps gave the height as 618 feet, but captured German maps, which later proved to be correct, gave the height as 702 feet. The trees and underbrush made excellent cover and yet were not dense enough to hinder effective machine gun fire. Strong supporting positions on both flanks made it impossible to work in from the sides, and left only one alternative—a frontal attack across open ground and uphill. The German defenses in the Bois-des-Loges consisted of many machine guns, alone and in nests, placed so as to fire in all directions and also support each other. It was impossible to attack one machine gun without coming under the fire of several others on either side of it.

The Grandpre stronghold was equally formidable, protected by three points—Talma Hill, the Aire River, and the citadel of Grandpre. The citadel was situated on a long, narrow tongue of land ending in a cliff about thirty feet high set in the middle of the town. This tongue of land commanded the surrounding country within a radius of nearly a mile. At the foot and on the top of the cliff were groups of strongly-built machine gun nests. This citadel was the key to Grandpre; without it, Grandpre was only a death trap. The position was made still stronger by a loop which the Aire River makes to the north between Grandpre and Chevieres, making an assault from that flank impractical.

The night of the relief was intensely dark and rainy; god damn mud. The roads were jammed with transport and men going in both directions. During the night, telephonic orders came to attack at 1600 hours on 16 October, the time set for the completion of the relief. It was after five o'clock before this order reached some of the Regiments and from these it had to be sent out to the Battalions, whose exact locations were not known. Owing to the confusion incident to lack of guides from the division being relieved and the abominable weather conditions, the relief of some of the units was not completed until hours after the time set for the attack. And there would be no artillery preparation.

In this scenario BGen. Hearn would have objected had they stopped to provide artillery prep. "Fire first and shoot later" was the quip he shared with the young officers who had attended his lectures back at the academy. Meaning what, they would ask, and at that point in his talk Hearn would promote the mobility of artillery in offensive actions. Fire your way into the battlefield, he explained, gain your foothold and set up your shooting range. Communication then becomes the key to your success. Get information and command decisions as close to the front as possible. He stressed the need to coordinate with the infantry.

The shattered condition of the front made the exact location of the Germans uncertain, except as to their general direction. On the right the 78th made the attack as ordered, with two battalions advancing on the Bois-des-Loges from the southeast. The 303rd went into action with this group. Added to the difficulties of an attack against a strong position was complete ignorance of the ground, over which there had been no chance for reconnaissance. Water and mud were knee deep in many places, and everyone was tired out after the experience of the previous night and the lack of any sleep. God damn mud.

Despite these obstacles, the 78th got a foothold in the Bois-des-Loges and promptly dug in on the western side of the woods. Another battalion continued the advance to the Aire River at the north and west of the town. Troops pushed across the stream at this point under heavy enemy machine gun fire and also gained a foothold there. Information from Corps Headquarters indicated that the success of the whole military situation depended upon the 78th reaching the northern edge of the Bois-des-Loges. This would link the Division with the French and push the Germans away from the Aire River where the enemy had drawn the line for their stand.

At daybreak on 18 October, a section of the Battalion had clawed to within thirty yards of the northwest edge of the woods, flanking a line of machine gun nests midway through the woods. Desperate fighting continued in the woods all day, during which several officers of 307th and 308th artillery became casualties. Captain McGlothan, who was in a forward position with the trench mortar battery, was called to pull back to the line of 75mm howitzers, with orders to take command of both artillery units and keep the artillery in the thick of action. He told Alfonso to take charge of the mortar battery.

Before nightfall, strong enemy counter-attacks were met. The costly gain of ground that had been won earlier in the day was lost as the Germans overran the weaker spots in the thinly-stretched linkage of troops. The 303rd was surrounded and communication was cut off. Desperate hand-to-hand combat with the Germans sprang up at spots all around the mortar battery; there was no more gap between the two armies.

The mortar had been assembled in a portion of a ravine that had a small stream on the right where flooding had washed the embankment into a neat alcove providing protection on two sides. The bank was about four feet high. At this specific moment in time, Alfonso was frozen in place looking up at the German soldier who stood above him less than 10 feet away; he did not see the man, only the weapon that was about to kill him.

At that peculiar moment a series of events occurred that can be attributed only to an incongruent assembly of time. The ground began to shake with a ferocious force. Mud slid down the embankment bringing the German soldier barreling directly at him as Alfonso toppled backwards into the arms of one of the American soldiers that Alfonso had not seen running up behind him.

Alfonso did see the doughboy who had stepped past him catching the German in the stomach with his bayonet, with a stream of intestines pulling out of the body as the stunned enemy was tossed toward the left and the blade slide away. In the oddest connection of thoughts, Alfonso remembered the discussion of a stiletto showing no wounds.

And in an even odder moment, Alfonso felt a sense of belonging that could only be understood but never described. The soldier who had caught him, pushed Alfonso to his feet, gave him a quick tap on the back, said "got you covered, Chip," and rushed on. Could he really have known me, Alfonso wondered to himself, or was he using the nickname in a generic application. McGlothan had tagged him with that moniker and some acquaintances had begun to adopt it. The Italian pronunciation of his last name used the "key" sound, whereas American adaptation used "chee."

Alfonso was to learn later that it was credit to McGlothan that the ground shook. Having learned what was happening at the front lines he had just pulled back from, McGlothan knew exactly where to direct artillery fire that saturated the ground immediately to the front of the trench battery, cutting off German reinforcements and enabling the 78th to resecure the area. The extremely close application of that artillery fire provided that ground shaking experience. God damn mud, this time said with a thankful chuckle.

The attack was continued on the 19th. The 153rd artillery placed a heavy two-hour concentration fire on the remaining enemy machine gun positions in the northern portion

of the Bois-des-Loges and the ridge to the northwest. The enemy was keeping up an incessant fire with machine guns, which the 153rd succeeded in reducing by sending over great numbers of high explosives, shrapnel, and gas shells.

The 303rd was pulled back for a short breather with attention turning to Grandpre.

When the 78th arrived on the scene, the enemy held the citadel and all of the northern and eastern parts of the town. A small patrol had moved into the western end of the town to secure a foothold. In some of the houses the enemy held the upper stories and a sort of perpendicular warfare ensued. It took five days of house-to-house fighting to complete the capture of the rest of the town, except the citadel.

After two hours of artillery preparation, beginning at midnight on the 18th, an assault had been made against the citadel in Grandpre and against Talma Hill to the west. Two parties attacked the citadel; one was unable to scale the cliff because of machine gun fire from the Bois-de-Bourgogne, and a storm of hand grenades from the top of the cliff. The other party succeeded in reaching the top, only to be driven off by machine guns and grenades.

If it felt like the stalemate was holding up the war, it was by design. General Liggett was using the opportunity to replenish the unit strength with the presence of veterans who knew how to fight. Now it looked like the bottleneck at Grandpre might hold up the entire offensive he was planning to renew. There was a pause in the operations around Grandpre from the 20th to 23rd of October to permit a careful reconnaissance and study of the situation. A new attack was planned, calling for heavy destructive fire and a concentration of nonpersistent gas on the points to be attacked. A smoke screen was to be laid down to cover two converging attacks from Grandpre and Talma Hill.

Alfonso was pulled into the discussion because he had been given nominal charge of the 303rd and now was not the time to consider rank. McGlothan shared with him the plans, along with maps and reconnaissance photos; these had been shared around the make-shift table and now lay in a stack before Alfonso. As he stared at the photo that topped the stack—bombed-out ruins of Grandpre and the town center that was crowned by the citadel— he was inspired to offer a suggestion. He pointed to a spot in the photo and told McGlothan that they could place the mortar at that location and shoot the artillery shells in the high angle projection for which the trench mortar had been designed.

GRAND PRE - A view from the church tower, the Citadel is that tongue of high ground denoted by an arrow in the upper left of view.

"You are going to lollygag your way down the hill, assemble the mortar, and shoot Germans," McGlothan assessed in critical response. "Do you want to yell up and ask them for a 'time out' first." Alfonso explained the rest of his plan and McGlothan no longer was a cynic. Together they went to the Packard truck and found as expected in the compartments designated for the supplies:

12 Sheets, tracing paper.	1 Ink, blue, bottle.
6 Sheets, drawing paper.	1 Eraser.
1 Rule.	100 Tacks, thumb.
1 Scale, meter.	1 Compass, drawing.
1 Box, "Accessory".	1 Tape, decimeter.
1 Protractor, celluloid.	1 Square.
12 Pencils, colored.	1 Tripod, plane table.
3 Pencils, drawing.	1 Pen, drawing.
1 Ink, red, bottle.	

On their trek in to relieve the 77th, Alfonso had noticed a Mack truck pushed off to the side of a woodland trail. He took a crew back to the site and they used the Packard to pull the Mack back onto the trail and kept it tethered for their return trip. The Mack truck was stripped to its skeletal frame. Alfonso had remembered the radiator on the Mack was located behind the engine and for his idea to work that was exactly what he would need. Repairs were made to the engine and the 58mm mortar was bolted to the framework above the rear axle, with blocks pounded into the springs to lessen the bounce. The platform was used to construct a protective barrier, with barely enough space between the slats to see where the truck was being driven.

A close-up view of the Citadel. Note the high tongue of ground projecting from center of view towards the river. Here the Germans had a commanding sweep of the Aire River Valley below.

The mortar battery could begin firing immediately upon arrival at the spot where Alfonso intended to park the Mack truck. Coordinates would be dialed in in advance. In order to get to the parking place that Alfonso had identified, the truck would have to run a gauntlet of machine gun fire but upon reaching the bottom of the hill they would be below the angle for those guns. The Germans could not reposition those machine guns without exposing themselves to the covering fire and hopefully they would not have time to lock their aim on the moving target.

Hand grenades would be a problem. Alfonso hoped that the turtle cover he designed for the Mack would cause the grenades to roll far enough away to save lives and buy time. He had recalled the exact dimensions of the available timbers from his rote memorization of the manual back at Camp Dix, contributing to the accuracy of the drawing and subsequent structure. With a coordinated attack, an assault team would be moving into position to remove that hand-grenade pressure. The greatest unknown, McGlothan noted, was how many shells could be fired before the Mack would shake apart from the recoil. (In 1923, the Packard corporation filed for a patent on the design of a vehicle they proposed to build for the military which was remarkably similar to the drawing Alfonso had prepared).

On the 26th of October, Alfonso was accelerating that Mack truck downhill into the heart of Grandpre, pushing the vehicle forward with every ounce of nervous energy that he had in his reserve.

The attack began the next morning as scheduled and was partially successful. The forces on top of Talma Hill began the attack which was preceded by a brief artillery diversion to the east and a ten minute preparation by the 75mm artillery and machine guns, the latter being especially effective, during which time Alfonso made his daring drive.

The men of the 78th easily gained the edge of the Bois-de-Bourgogne, and then fought their way along to a line running along the edge of the woods to a point about a quarter mile east of Talma Hill. This left a gap of almost a mile between the forces in battlefield north of Grandpre, with the battalion coming in from the west.

The support troops in Grandpre encountered terrific machine gun and artillery fire, so much so that their advance was badly broken up and the assault team did not find position to provide cover from dropping grenades. Lieutenant M. H. Harris and four men were able to scale the wall of the citadel in time to accompany the rolling barrage. This small group reached Bellejoyeuse Ferme and was able to provide the crossfire that snared the Germans. Seventy-eight prisoners were taken on the citadel; Lt. Harris and his men taking forty-seven of them out of one dugout.

This is what was left of the buildings on BELLEJOYEUSE FARM when captured by the 78th Division.

The Mack truck survived the onslaught. Hand grenades bounced away as had been hoped, with a shrapnel slash received by one of the three battery mates who had huddled beneath the protective cover with the mortar and roared into Grandpre with Alfonso fighting the steering wheel most of the way. As expected, the tires were shot out and steering the beastly Mack was a challenge. The stronghold of Grandpre was taken, opening the way to the success which followed.

The targeted assistance of 75mm artillery drove the last remaining enemy machine guns from the heights north of Grandpre, pushing the Germans away from this sector that had figured so conspicuously in holding up the extreme left of the American line.

During the last few days of October, preparations were made for the big attack of November 1st. Quantities of small arms, ammunition, rockets, flares, etc., were brought up close to the lines and stored in dumps. Telephone lines were increased and new lamp stations organized so that communication would be assured during the attack. The 303rd engineers under constant fire built several bridges across the Aire River; Alfonso helped.

The artillery force was restored to a great degree by merging French batteries into their mix. The only thing that was lacking to put the Division in better shape was men to replace the heavy casualties of the 153rd Field Artillery.

chapter nine

A replacement driver did arrive for the roster vacancy created by the loss of the commander's chauffer—Pfc. Samuel E. Adams of Shuff, Virginia. The enthusiastic welcome that might have been expected was replaced by a stoic stare as Alfonso greeted Sam with a measure of reservation and formality.

"No questions," Sam softly said. "I understand."

With that simple acknowledgement, a slight nod of his head and Sam's own shell-shocked look as their eyes met, Alfonso dropped to a knee and cried for the first and only time in uniform. This was not the way to greet a friend. A bit later after composure had been restored and accounts current, Sam gave Alfonso a copy of the photograph they had stood for in the innocence of not even a year past.

Alfonso realized that he had been treating the war like a dirty job that had to be finished when fighting war really was an emotional experience.

His unit was not alone in the fight, Sam reminded him. He noted that the 80th Division and in particular, the 155mm howitzer manned by Battery F of the 315th Field Artillery Regiment, had been firing its guns and moving forward inch by inch every day since the shooting began on 26 September. That was the unit to which Alfonso originally had been assigned. (By the end of the war, that Battery was in battle for 46 consecutive days, the longest stretch of service for an artillery unit in the war).

During the last days of October the front line of the 78th division stretched out along the St. Juvin-Grandpre Road and along the crest of the ridge in the southern portion of the Bois-de-Bourgogne to the village of Talma. The sector was quieter than it had been during the last two weeks of fighting.

The Germans still sent over their morning and evening "hate" and dropped big shells harmlessly into the valley of the Aire. Enemy planes occasionally flew low along the front line, firing machine guns with little effect. Stray bullets came down from the woods north and northeast of Talma, cracking over the heads of the outposts. But there was little organized firing. Talma and Grandpre had been cleared and the Bois-des-Loges which had proved such a stronghold against earlier attacks was as quiet. It was believed the enemy had withdrawn its rear guard; however, patrols sent forward during the night of 31 October found them still in position.

Alfonso knew first hand why the Americans were waiting to charge. The First Army was preparing for a 1 November attack, and Alfonso was privy to the secret plans and maps; he was welcomed as a full participant at the daily meetings with line officers at command posts and Division Headquarters. At Brigade Headquarters the intelligence reports were being analyzed with the greatest care. The artillery Regiments were bringing up vast supplies of ammunition. Every detail was being carefully prepared as if the men were getting ready to mine coal. Alfonso recognized the emotions and appreciated the systematic thought.

In brief the plan of attack was as follows: in front lay the Bois-de-Bourgogne, a belt of thick woods extending north for about eight kilometers. Fighting through this forest was to be avoided by saturating it with yperite (mustard gas), especially along its eastern edge.

The first objective was a line stretching from the Bois-de-Bourgogne on the left, through the northern edge of the Bois-des-Loges; the subsequent objective, a ridge two kilometers north of Briquenay. As the Bois-des-Loges was believed to be thinly held, two hours artillery preparation was thought to be adequate. During all this preparation, the mysterious symbols of "D" Day and "H" Hour were the only information that was given out for the moment to 'jump-off.'

A road leading into ill-fated GRAND PRE.

Top- Sheller holes dug by our men on slope of GRAND PRE-ST. JUVIN road, just south of BOIS DES LOGES. Bottom - gun crews in action.

On 30 October the wail of gas shells from the 153rd artillery told Alfonso that the yperite was beginning its deadly work in the Bois-de-Bourgogne. All that day and all the next the gas fire continued unceasingly. Nearly forty thousand rounds of yperite shell were fired into certain areas of the Bourggogne Woods, then batteries concentrated destructive fire on certain known enemy positions. The continued rapid whirr of shells passing over to the German lines turned day and night of 31 October into a weird pandemonium. For two hours immediately preceding the attack, ten thousand rounds of high explosive were poured into the troublesome Bois-des-Loges by the 153rd F. A. Brigade and the attached French artillery. As further fire preparation, the 303rd laid down a heavy mortar barrage on the Bois-des-Loges, the ridge to the west of this woods and on the road running north into le Morthomme from Grandpre. Under this intense concentration it seemed impossible that the Germans could survive.

The night of the 31st, word was whispered down the front line to Alfonso and crew that the H Hour was five-thirty the next morning. Great confidence prevailed among the men of the 303rd; morale was excellent. The success of their jerry-rigged mortar truck had restored the spirits of everyone. Newly promoted Major McGlothan said in a conference of officers for final preparation that tomorrow's show would be a "picnic," and, he believed, the last battle of the war. The major was right in his second prophecy, but the picnic was a little delayed. He had underestimated the enemy's brilliant rear-guard defense in the Bois-des-Loges. On 1 November a rested and replenished First Army renewed the offensive with a thunderous predawn barrage. The 1st and 3rd Corps attacked vigorously on the left and right flanks, setting the stage for a three-division smash through the center by the 5th Corps that sent the Germans into retreat. The Air Service roared in to strafe and bomb in an example of the ground-air coordination that General Liggett had insisted upon. The German center virtually evaporated within the overwhelming aggression of the American First Army which advanced an astonishing five miles at a number of breakout places across the front lines.

The driving attack progressed splendidly for the 78th Division and supporting 153rd Artillery until the unimproved road running east and west through the woods was reached; here further progress was checked by murderous machine gun fire from countless German Maxim guns echeloned in depth to the front and on the heights to the northwest. Such was the natural strength of the German positions, combined with the admirable advantage the enemy had taken of the terrain. Alfonso realized that previous artillery preparation in the Bois-des-Loges had been a wasted effort. Everywhere numerous shell craters were in evidence and so were the barking, snapping German machine guns.

Night came and with it a new plan of attack. The way was now open for the Bois-des-Loges to be attacked from the west. The infantry moved up during the night into position in the vicinity of Ferme-de-Loges to strike this stronghold on the flank at the same time that the 153rd Field Artillery Brigade renewed its attack from the south. The maneuver worked, a major breach in the line was opened and the Germans abandoned their weapons and began a full retreat.

Alfonso learned first-hand why the enemy had been able to put up their stand. During the heavy artillery concentrations, the Germans had promptly withdrawn their guns until the storm of shells had passed. They had dropped their guns into deep dugouts during the bombardments and with cables hoisted them back into place and turned them on the advancing infantry immediately after the bombardment was over. Deep buried in the woods were carefully dug and skillfully protected dugouts and emplacements. Beside the Maxims and plentiful supplies of ammunition, the Germans in their haste had left helmets, packs, pistols, personal equipment, wine and maps in reckless and wholesale abandon. Alfonso and crew scooped up what bounty the trucks could handle and headed off in pursuit. Sam drove the White; the new guy—Alfonso never could remember his name—previously had taken over as driver of the general's staff car.

A detachment consisting of several companies of infantry jumped on the trucks with the mortar battery. The now mobile unit rushed forward until they were stopped by mined roads and blown out bridges north of Briquenay. The infantry pushed on while Alfonso and the trench battery team helped engineers restore the road to passable shape. To retard pursuit, the Germans had felled great trees which had lined the roads into crisscross obstacles; in certain sections, numerous rows had been chopped with a huge V near the base, ready to be dropped, but the installation of the necessary spark wire and explosive discharge were neglected in their haste. Roads were blown up, bridges destroyed and the steel rails at close intervals shattered and twisted by explosive charges. The 303rd engineers now showed why they were indispensable; the ability of the First Army to continue pursuit after the break through, required prompt clearing up and repair of the shattered roads and hastily constructing temporary bridges. Alfonso and the motorized team now numbering five trucks, assisted in this work and then pushed on in an effort to keep up with the advancing infantry.

All day on the 3rd of November the advance of the 78th infantry continued steady and rapid. Night brought the front line to a point in front of Briquenay stretching through the northern edge of the Thenorgues Woods. The advance was so fast that all communications with the rear, including, of course, ration and ammunition supply, had been temporarily cut off. The night was cold and a constant drizzling rain wet and chilled the men. God damn mud. Alfonso with most of his 303rd contingent had kept pace.

McGlothan noted that the Germans responded mostly as had been expected; finding their right and left outflanked, the enemy had no choice but disengagement and headlong retreat. Several times in the next few days when the Germans attempted to set up a defense line, the Americans overran it before the enemy could issue orders to man it. The enemy with German rigidity adhered to the directives of their structured chain-of-command. Americans moved with information at the front. McGlothan gleefully reported that a Regiment commander in the 2nd Division had led his troops through the woods at night pushing them past the Germans who were setting up to receive their charge; the enemy surrendered in the morning when they realized their guns were pointed the wrong way. The Meuse River became the one hope to contain the American surge, but that vanished when the 5th Division raced over open ground, forded the river, and secured a crossing that ripped wider as American force pushed through. Now orders were received to make an all-out charge to recapture the city of Sedan. McGlothan explained that capturing the rail lines that passed through Sedan would cut the German army in half, eliminating their logistical support and access to natural resources from the coal mines.

The German rear guard had mined a wide, filled road covering a stretch of nearly one-half kilometer from the road fork just north of Briuelles to the fork near the southwest tongue of the Bois-de-Sy. This rear guard strategy worked exceptionally well for the Germans, as it effectively blocked the advance of the artillery and transport. The heavy charges had blown the immense rock boulders forming the road bed far to both sides of the roadway and left huge, gaping holes at intervals of about 20 yards. The 303rd engineers urgently began construction of a corduroy road crossing the low, swampy marsh ground alongside the ruined portions, which enabled the 303rd Trench Mortar Battery to proceed. Alfonso was never to see McGlothan again.

chapter ten

The enemy destruction did stop the 78th Division. At this point in the war, forces of the 42nd Division led by Brigadier General Douglas MacArthur caught up with the 78th and relieved the infantry from the line with the artillery ordered to continue the push. Alfonso already had raced ahead with his trucks, expecting that his supply line would catch up to him. They were just clearing a hilltop when the sounds and smells of battle caught their senses; Alfonso was aware that the enemy was not far ahead. Just then the Packard began to sputter; Alfonso coasted to the bottom of the hill and into a field at the side of the road where he could get out of the way of the other motor vehicles as the convoy moved on. He waited with truck and crew. They had not long to wait. An officer's staff car crested the hill, sped to where the Packard was parked and without preamble politely asked in military parlance what the hell they were doing sitting here when the war was just ahead.

"General, sir," Alfonso began. "This truck runs on two things—gas and imagination, and we still have plenty of imagination left." MacArthur frowned, spoke quietly under his breathe to his chauffer instructing him to get the gas can, and said to Alfonso. "Effective immediately you are transferred to the 42nd; follow me."

American divisions began a race to have their troops be the first to enter the city of Sedan. General Liggett began to regret his earlier suggestion that fictional no-crossing signs be removed from assigned sectors. The 1st Division cut off the 42nd Division in the dark and confusion reigned. BGen. MacArthur had pushed well into the night and men and machines all needed a brief respite. Once again Alfonso was awakened from a deep slumber as he lay asleep under his truck. He heard MacArthur barking commands in response to commands that were being barked at him. The general did not have his pants to his knees, but he did have a patrol of American soldiers aiming their rifles at him; they accused MacArthur of being a German spy. Even after Alfonso and others spoke up, they did not relent until their own commander arrived on the scene.

Men from both Divisions pushed on and held the slopes looking into Sedan as French troops were permitted the pleasure of reclaiming the key city that had been taken from them a long time ago. The Germans requested an armistice; fighting ended at 1100 hours on 11 November. The Meuse-Argonne Offensive cost 26,277 American lives lost and 95,786 wounded.

Alfonso, Sam and 40 other members of the 303rd were sent to Imecourt, France, and officially transferred to the 117th Trench Mortar Battery on 16 November, numbering among the 50 replacements that brought the unit back to full strength. The 117th was a storied National Guard unit out of Baltimore, Maryland. It would be a stretch to say the new men were welcomed; they were nothing more than replacement parts.

The 117th had been in France since October 1917, the same month Alfonso had reported to Camp Lee. The 117th was part of the 42nd Rainbow Division, named because the National Guard units that were combined to form the Division had been drawn from a large number of States, a rainbow of states according to its commander, BGen. MacArthur. Most of the original men had a wound of one sort or another; they had lost many friends.

The men transferred from the 303rd and their motor trucks were greeted with a measured animosity upon arrival because to that point of the war the 117th Trench Mortar Battery had been horse-drawn. The horses who had been cursed throughout the time in battle, now were drawing tears from some of the hardened veterans who were saying goodbye to a trusted colleague.

The newly augmented 117th, now assigned as part of the Army of Occupation, sped into Belgium on 21 November, stopped near the town of Frassem and bivouacked in a muddy field. God damn mud. Alfonso was standing in line for morning chow when one of the 117th veterans slipped on the embankment at the top of the field kitchen; although Alfonso caught him before he fell, his foot sank into the five-gallon pot that held the coffee. Alfonso helped him stand up and take a place in the chow line while the mess sergeant quickly scooped a glob of mud and horse dung from atop the brewing coffee. Alfonso and the veteran both politely refused the offer of coffee and moved on to the other breakfast treats. The veteran introduced himself—Dr. Henry A. McMains, a veteran of the Spanish-American War who had attached himself to the unit as a volunteer with the YMCA. By an accident of the god damn mud, Alfonso had made himself a lifelong friend.

The battery left Frassem on the 23 November, crossed into Luxembourg where they stayed for a day before returning to the Belgium town of Arlon where they were assigned to guard railroad cars and captured German artillery. While the Battery remained in Arlon, the rest of the 42nd Division advanced into Germany. Rations were getting low and Thanksgiving Day arrived with a meal of corn-willie and hardtack for the feast. Alfonso was with the group of grumbling men who decided to open the railroad boxcars to see what it was that they were guarding. They were led in their search by that grizzly veteran, Dr. McMains.

In their scavenge they found barrels of potatoes and cabbage. Alfonso found the mess sergeant and made a suggestion. He worked with the kitchen staff, Dr. McMains, and other volunteers, to mix up the ingredients to cook a huge batch of halupki that would become the centerpiece of their holiday meal. Following a recipe that he had watched his mother use many times, available meats were ground up, then browned with diced onions and garlic. Chopped potatoes, rice, salt and pepper, and a few eggs for combining the ingredients, all were stirred into the mix for filling. The cabbages were cored, then boiled to soften the leaves. The cabbage leaves that loosened from their ball were moved to a cooling bowl. Alfonso demonstrated how to remove the vein of the cabbage leaf with the flick of a neatly sharped knife, producing a level platform ideal for rolling up the handful of the filling mix that he placed at the center. Place the veined end of the leaf over the fill, tuck in the sides, and roll it up.

All of the cabbage pieces yet unused, the cores, veins and unused leaves, were placed at the bottom of the huge mess pan and covered with a mix of tomato sauce and water from the boiled cabbage. A ham bone was placed in the middle as the finished product was brought to a boil and left to simmer. Halupki.

There were standing orders forbidding pilfering; subsequently, each man in the 117th battery was 'asked' to make a donation to pay for the foodstuffs. Dr. McMains ran the purchase through the YMCA and the division commander was satisfied. The battery packed up their leftover halupki, cabbage and potatoes, along with other needed items that had been pilfered from the now-resealed boxcars, and departed on 6 December for a 10-day journey through a string of German towns, arriving at Kreuzberg. The battery was assigned to barracks that had been built as a bunkhouse for railroad men. The barracks were composed of small, neat rooms, each containing four to six single bunks. Alfonso found some clean white sheets, and with clean clothes and somewhat regular baths, he was scratching far fewer cooties. Even his hearing was begin to return to normal; for two months—11 September to 11 November—he had experienced the drumming tattoo of artillery fire varying only in intensity and rhythm.

As Christmas approached, the mess sergeant boarded the Packard with Alfonso and they drove through the countryside scouring for foodstuffs that would make their Christmas dinner. They found a farmer who sold them a young bovine for 200 marks and 12 bars of soap. Soap had become a valuable commodity, worth its weight in gold, literally. One of the officers had found a well-stocked wine cellar and a large quantity was confiscated and hauled aboard the truck.

Alfonso celebrated the attainment of his 24th year of his birth. He celebrated his long-awaited promotion to the non-commissioned rank of Wagoneer, effective 1 December. He celebrated the holiday. He celebrated the end of the war, taking his staggered stand on German soil. He celebrated clean cloths, the return of hearing, the lack of cooties; he even celebrated the god damn mud. He drank little in observing the arrival of 1919, still nursing his hangover from previous celebrations.

On the morning of 9 January 1919 all motor equipment, ammunition and supplies were turned over to the 67th Field Artillery and Alfonso boarded a train with members of the 117th for transport to Torfou, France. Alfonso felt the loss of his Packard in much the same way others had missed their horses, but he shed no tears. He was ready to go home. Alfonso would have to wait his turn; he was one of two million men for whom shipping arrangements needed to be made. The schedule was spelled out in February, when General Order #35 was published to announce the sailing schedule for all American Divisions. The 117th Trench Mortar Battery would depart for home in April.

The Battery stayed at Torfou for three months. During that time French civil authorities called attention to an old law enacted on 23 August 1863 which decreed—"loi sur la police de la circulation et al conservation des routes"—which they explained meant that when a thaw follows a hard frost, roads will suffer damage which is often irreparable if heavy traffic is permitted to circulate before they have had time to settle. Made sense; also made for routine work for Alfonso as he again helped keep the road in repair.

One night the principal café in town was raided and looted of most of its wines and liquors. The demijohns containing spirits were hidden in a nearby pond where, by tying strings to the handles of the jugs and fastening corks to the other ends they could be located easily. The café proprietor threatened to sue the United States government; every man in the battery was taxed to pay for the loss. Alfonso would not admit to any crime, but he did not object to paying his share.

The Division organized schools for a variety of subjects—English for the foreign born, all grammar school branches, agriculture, black-smithing, motor repair, wireless telegraphy, electrical wiring, and other trades. Dr. McMains encouraged Alfonso to attend as many classes as possible. Alfonso polishing his English and assured himself that he was current in vehicle repair; he even assisted teaching in many of those classes. Many recreational activities were provided—athletics, vaudeville, motion pictures, dances, horse-shows—most of which held little interest for Alfonso. He was more concerned with news from home that the 18th amendment had been passed into law, prohibiting liquor; it was passed by Congress on 18 December 1917, and ratified on 16 January 1919. Section 1 stated:

> "After one year from the ratification of this article the manu-facture, sale, or transportation of intoxicating liquors within, the importation thereof into, or the exportation thereof from the United States and all territory subject to the juris-diction thereof for beverage purposes is hereby prohibited."

Alfonso was most concerned about what impact the law would have on his family; how could anyone explain to Egisto that it would be illegal to make wine. Admittedly, perhaps shamefully, in the midst of his revelry during those leisure days early in the post war he had not thought much about events in Pennsylvania. Or events anywhere in the world for that matter. When the revelry began to dull, much of the conversation began to shift.

As he extended his reach for the wine bottle that was being passed around, Dr. McMains asked, "Did you ever wonder why we had to get into this fight?"

"I had no choice," Alfonso retorted. "I was drafted." He hesitated a brief moment to burp, and in his succinct manner, added, "money," interrupted by another expulsion, "and the toughest guy on the block."

"Right you are," McMains replied as he seized the conversation to espouse on his view of the war, "on both expressions. The history books will report that the war was caused by the assassination of that Austria-Hungary prince in Serbia. That is too simple; the answer is by far more complex. McMains began to piece together an ongoing dialogue they had been having over the past several days.

"We are facing a new world order. Nationalism—defined as an intense form of patriotism or loyalty to one's country." The problem, McMains said, is that nationalists exaggerate the value and importance of their home country, placing its interests over and above those of other nations.

"That is what those big guys did. The empires of Britain, France, Austria-Hungary, and the Ottomans used their resources to push progress to all corners of the civilized world, creating a global economy.

"Instead of sharing the wealth, the empires turned to exploiting the resources for their own gain.

"This created an us-against-them attitude. For nations this meant a belief in their own cultural, economic and military supremacy. For individuals this is expressed as a tribe mentality, with intense loyalty inwards and aggression outwards."

McMains continued to explain. "In many ways the world fell victim to progress. We are building machines that can do the work of a dozen men," he said. "This means a lot of idle time for displaced workers. And thanks to the invention of the linotype, those idle workers are reading all kinds of propaganda."

Alfonso knew that Dr. McMains was referencing the hot-metal line casting machine that had been introduced to printing plants in 1886 by Ottmar Mergenthaler. The ability to typeset entire lines in a single casting revolutionized the printing industry, resulting in massive amounts of information reaching all levels of society, with daily news now reaching most civilized people.

"In matters of foreign affairs or global competition, many were convinced that their country was fair, righteous and beyond fault or blame," McMains continued. "Nationalists demonized rival nations, characterizing them as aggressive, scheming, deceitful, backward or uncivilized. Nationalist press reports convinced many readers that the interests of their country were being threatened by the plotting, scheming and hungry imperialism of its rivals."

Sam Adams joined the conversation and summarized the agreed upon facts of military overconfidence that shaped the dialogue:

- The British believed their naval power, coupled with the size and resources of the British Empire, would give them the upper hand in any war. Being an island also isolated Britain from invasion or foreign threat.

- German leaders placed great faith in Prussian military efficiency, the nation's powerful industrial base, her new armaments and her expanding fleet of battleships and U-boats (submarines).

- In Russia, Tsar Nicholas II believed his empire was sustained by God and protected by a massive standing army of 1.5 million men, the largest peacetime land force in Europe. Russian commanders believed the country's enormous population gave it the upper hand over the smaller nations of western Europe.

- The French placed their faith in the country's heavy industry, which had expanded rapidly in the late 1800s. Paris also placed great stock in its defenses, particularly a wall of concrete barriers and fortresses running the length of its eastern border.

"Voltaire said that God is always on the side of the big battalions," Dr. McMains said by way of segue to the larger message he was trying to share. "What he meant was that the side that can build the biggest military by amassing tanks, guns, ships, airplanes, and munitions productions is the side that will win. That was us. Not because we manufactured so much weaponry, which we did, but because we were able to maintain our army.

"We call this the Great War, but really a better title would be the 'Total War.' Before 1914, Total War was not possible because people lived much closer to subsistence. Too many people were required to labor in the fields and workshops just to feed and clothe the population; it cost too much for governments to sustain an army in mass combat.

"War has been redefined, with multi-million man armies remaining in the field for years, giving and accepting appalling losses without the army disintegrating. That is Total War. We won because Austria-Hungary, Turkey, and Germany all ran short of food long before they ran out of guns and shells. That is because of the negative impact that mobilization for war had on agriculture production by the peasants. Resources—particularly men and horses—were redirected away from farming. Once in the army, these men and horses still needed to be fed, requiring diversion of food supplies from rural households to government warehouses.

"The problem was much of the farming was accomplished by peasants who grew food mostly for their own sustenance, using their excess production to buy manufactured goods. The war dried up access to manufactured goods, and with most able-bodied men off to war, peasants grew or gathered only what they needed to survive. Major food production supported the army, squeezing people living in the cities; food prices soared and urban famine set in."

Alfonso quizzed, "how does this bring us a new world order."

"Insightful, my young friend," McMains roared in delight, made all the more boisterous with the opening of another bottle of wine.

He explained that another form of nationalism was on the rise. "It is that nationalism that caused the world to go the war, and it is that nationalism that will shape our future.

"This nationalism is not about the supremacy of a nation, but rather it is about the rights of the ethnic groups who people those nations. They want the individual freedoms that we Americans have begun to take for granted."

He explained that pan-Slavism, a belief that the Slavic peoples of eastern Europe should have their own nation, was a powerful force in the region, especially in Serbia. Proponents of the pan-Slavic movement were particularly opposed to the control and influence of the Austro-Hungarian Empire and hoped to drive the monarchy from the Balkans and establish a 'Greater Serbia' that would unify all Slavic people. It was this pan-Slavic nationalism that inspired the assassination of Archduke Franz Ferdinand in Sarajevo in June 1914, the event that led directly to the outbreak of the war.

"So we fought this war so that all nations could govern themselves like we do in America?" Adams asked.

"That will never happen," McMains said in blunt conclusion. "We Americans are defined by our individualism. Each American is different, and that is what makes us the same in the eyes of the rest of the world."

Alfonso could see that the discussion was beyond the comprehension of Adams, but he intuitively understood what McMains was explaining. The 'tribal' instinct that drew the people of different nations into cohesiveness was based on communal living that had evolved from time immemorial. Rules of social order began with the monarchy at the top of society and were extended to the populace through the hierarchy of the social classes. People knew their place, but they also knew they were part of a greater whole and consequently could find a sense of belonging in the embrace of their commune family.

"The true American is someone who is fiercely independent," McMains insisted, "and one who values our greatest freedom—our freedom of thought.

"Americans are free to form our own opinions," McMains continued. "You should base those opinion on evidence. Trust the science.

"Never, ever let someone else do your thinking. Not the government, nor any religious zealot.

Alfonso drifted away from the conversation to a trance of self-reflection. He began to replay conversations from days past, mixed with snippets of comments from family.

Americans are disposable units. "We are nothing more than economic slaves," Alfonso had argued, comparing the plight of immigrants to the treatment of Africans that had been enslaved in the southern states of America. Dr. McMains did not dispute the logic as he had listened to Alfonso rant about the control coal mine owners exerted through their company-run stores, company police, and company doctors.

The more his thinking evolved, the more Alfonso held to his own contemplation. We are told in the company-run schools that America is the land of opportunity. Opportunity for what? he asked himself. Freedom. That means an individual is free to do good, but equally free to do evil, as one seeks a place in the social order.

One of the few letters that Alfonso had received from his older brother Dario read: "Life is one great big shit sandwich; the more bread you have, the less shit you eat." Communities throughout America were built with the singular purpose of making money. Endearment to a tribe or family was not part of equation.

Alfonso reflected on advice his mother had offered. "A group of thoughtful, committed people can change the world; change can happen in no other way." His mother also had cautioned to beware of the power of stupid in large groups. "Education can fix ignorance," she said, "but you cannot cure stupid."

Americans are defined as an individual by how they spend their money, McMains had opined. Company owners and corporation executives can spend money to improve the lives of workers; they were equally free to spend money on themselves. The golden rule, Dario had quipped; "those who have the gold, rule."

The wisest spendthrifts invested their money in workers, not because of an affinity for the populace, but moreso to maximize the 'unit' before it becomes disposable. What will happen when the company town no longer is needed? Alfonso again asked himself, are communities as disposable as the workers?

Yes. The affirmative response was swift to conclude his thinking. The town will have satisfied its purpose. What remains will be defined by the money that remains in that community. Individuals will have to establish themselves as part of the local economy;

those who cannot reestablish themselves will disperse into another American setting where their work is needed to grow the economy.

Then we are nothing more than economic slaves. He considered to himself, have I not proved my point?

The thoughts were unsettling for Alfonso as he continued to process self-consciousness. His belonging to his family was given; commitment to community was a choice. Except that he was given little choice when drafted into the army. Lots of ideas were dancing around in his head.

The problem, Alfonso concluded, was that although he could not clearly state the question, he intuitively knew where he should begin his search to find some answers.

Every man had an opportunity to experience a 10-day all expenses paid leave along the Riviera beach—the coastal cities of Nice, Cannes, Monaco, and Menton were filled with American soldiers. Special leaves also were being granted to men to visit England, Belgium, Switzerland, Italy, and other European countries for the purpose of seeing relatives. 10-day leave, all expenses paid.

After due reflection, Alfonso made the request and continued beyond the Riviera for a return to Ponte Della Venturina, Grana-glione, Pistoia, Italy, the place of his beginning. He began his leave the second week of March 1919.

chapter eleven

The name was Chiappore. This was an ancient designation assigned to a community of workers who operated a tannery along the Val di Bura River. The title can be traced to the Etruscans, the first inhabitants of this remote mountainous region that at the time of their settlement had been a marshland. An inhabitant of this village of Chiappore, one who was called Ulvieri, was singled out for his service to the Catholic Church and through affiliation with the House of Savoy had been given the name Chiappelli. This is the paternal line that followed to Alfonso. This is how this became so.

Alfonso Giuseppe Carlo Chiappelli had ample time for self-reflection as the train removed him from the umbrella of discipline that made him part of the United States Army and presented him with a renewed view of his ancestral lands. He was somewhat aware of the storied past of his forbearers; every family he knew had a similar story to tell and various pieces of the past hung out like unexploded canisters. There were a few other American soldiers aboard the train, not from the same units but all sharing the same pilgrimage.

If there was any question of his loyalties, the honest answer would be that Alfonso straddled the fence as the Chiappelli family had done for generations. The family had a long affiliation with the House of Savoy which straddled the border of France and Italy. The family held neutral in the hostilities of the Neri and Bianchi that engulfed Pistoia. He was born and lived his first years in Granaglione, a small town that straddled the border of the regions of Emilio-Romagna and Pistoia; this dividing line marked the demarcation between the rule of the Papacy and the Republic. Pistoia had been under the influence of Florence, ruled by the Medici family.

It was this immensity of thought that held Alfonso captive as he stepped onto the train platform at Granaglione, the home of his birth. What he remembered as active bustle of an expansive community had shrunk to a tiny hamlet of homes along both sides of the Reno River. Alfonso was 8 years old when he had departed for America from that very spot. Although young, early childhood memories stuck with Alfonso and flooded back with each step he took along worn paths leading between worn buildings, bringing him to a worn-out town center.

The contrast with his new life was stunning. In America, Alfonso had grown to maturity in planned communities where the infrastructure that was installed to support the mining industry included not only housing but also facilities for education, religion, commerce, and entertainment—with planned obsolescence reflected in the seemingly temporary nature of all construction. Whereas in Granaglione, the community cast a vision of permanence with structures remaining from ancient time when inhabitants merged at that site for mutual protection; even the barns and storage sheds were constructed with stone and brick, with thickly thatched roofs that had been holding back the weather for hundreds of years. Infrastructure such as water, sewage, or electricity were add-on after thoughts, installed with less consistency.

Alfonso registered in at the osteria that once had been operated by his parents and now was owned and managed by the Vivarelli family, cousins through his paternal line. The clerk was rather stiff and formal and offered no recognition or acknowledgement of the Chiappelli name that Alfonso had announced when he signed in. The day was early and he had slept comfortably on the train, so Alfonso opted for a nourishing Tuscan breakfast of pulenda, served with fresh sheep milk ricotta. Pulenda was made from chestnut flour, a staple for the people of the Apennine Mountains. His father often said that chestnuts were the secret to a long life for Tuscans because it gave them good teeth, good health, and something to eat when others might go hungry. This was particularly true now. During the war when many able-bodied men went off to war, crops were not planted; there was no wheat, so there was no bread, nor pasta.

The recall of roasted chestnuts caused Alfonso to drift into clips of memories from his early life in Granaglione where every big fireplace had a chestnut pan with holes in the bottom, handmade by the local blacksmith, hanging up at the side of the fireplace. His mother had a method for preserving the fresh chestnuts for as long as possible; she soaked them in water for 8 days, changing the water either daily or every other day, then laid the chestnuts out on the aia (the flat stone work space in front of the house that separates the house from the fields) to dry in the sun. After that they were taken into the cellar and piled up in a corner and covered with sand. This preserved them long enough to make roasted chestnuts from the time they were harvested in October and November through to Easter.

At the conclusion of his breakfast, he asked for an order of succiole to enjoy during his hike to the Villa di Cireglio, home of the Chiappelli for more than 500 years. Uncle Umberto, a younger brother to Egisto, now occupied the family homestead. Although 10 years younger than Egisto, Umberto was the second son and next in line to take over after Egisto migrated to America. Chestnuts boiled with wild fennel for flavoring were called "succiole" because they are eaten by sucking the flesh of the chestnut from a hole poked in the rind. The chestnuts must be boiled for a very, very long time.

Alfonso sensed that he was being followed as he hiked a well-worn path that bisected the designated roads and reduced his hike by several miles. When he sat down to reset his boot, two men momentarily came into view; he had seen them before when he was eating his breakfast. Alfonso did not fear for his safety; his Uncle Umberto was a carabinieri, a police officer, and he felt the comfort of familiar surroundings—the complacency of being home.

Villa di Cireglio is a mountainside collection of homes developed in the Etruscan tradition with understated magnificence.

A serpentine trail leads up a long sloping plateau that connects Cireglio to the bountiful Po Valley plains of Pistoia and on a clear day provides a view beyond the valley to the city of Prato. The trail outlines olive groves, vineyards, and other staples of Tuscan life.

Alfonso instantly recognized his Uncle standing in patio of the villa and he quickly strode the remaining paces; his uncle had visited America during the emigration of the youngest brother, Uncle Pio, 10 years earlier. The huge smile Alfonso shared quickly disappeared when the first words from Umberto were a gruffly spoken question, "why have you come back here?" Alfonso had sent word in advance, so his arrival should not have been a surprise. "This is not your home."

"Can I not come back for a visit?" Alfonso asked. After he made it clear to his Uncle that he had not returned to make a claim to the family homestead, and that his stay would be temporary, his Uncle relaxed enough to provide the courtesy expected by a guest to his home. "These are uncertain times," Umberto said by way of an apology. "We are in the midst of a social revolution."

When Alfonso mentioned the two men that had followed behind him on the trail from Granaglione, Umberto admitted that they were two of his deputies. Alfonso asked why his uncle felt it necessary to have him watched over, his uncle chuckled into his response that Alfonso was not singled out—Umberto had deputies watching over all soldiers returning from the war, suspecting that some might be bringing back disruptive ideas. Umberto had net-worked with many others in the carabinieri organization to provide an enforcement arm to a new political force that was taking charge throughout the Italian Peninsula. In fact, the defacto leader of this effort, Benito Mussilini, was scheduled to announce the following week on 23 March 1919 the formation of the National Fascist Party.

Despite the uncomfortable dialogue with his uncle, as he settled into his visit other relatives and family friends in the close community began to appear in the courtyard to pay their respects and provide Alfonso with the welcome home that he had hoped to receive. His cousin Tosca could not keep her beautiful big brown eyes off of him; she was the 10-year-old daughter of Umberto and his wife Diadema. Unfortunately, Alfonso could not keep his eyes off of the visible bruises on Diadema that marked Umberto as a brute. Alfonso cut his visit short, but was pleased to be accompanied back along the trail by well-wishers who out of their amazement and curiosity wanted to chat with an American soldier who had ventured into their midst. They all had laughed when one in their number observed out loud that Alfonso spoke Italian with an American accent. In response Alfonso laughed to himself that they spoke Italian with an accent that was quite distinct to the Tuscan region.

Upon arrival back at the osteria in Granaglione, Alfonso was greeted by a young man who looked oddly familiar as he stepped forward to impede the way. "I hope you might remember me," he said, "we played together as children when we gathered at your grandfather's estate."

"Riccardo Chiappelli," Alfonso said simultaneous with his cousin by way of renewed acquaintance, Alfonso immediately remembering that the father of Riccardo was the family representative to the House of Savoy and titled Conti (Count) Chiappelli. "I came to claim you," Riccardo said, "and take you to a family reunion of sorts."

"I have already checked you out of the osteria," he added, as an assistant who was attending to Riccardo stepped forth holding the U.S. Army issued duffle bag into which Alfonso had crammed his supplies for the trip. "Sorry to rush you, but we have to hurry if we are going to catch the last train to Pistoia. I will explain on the way." The bodyguard stood professional, in sharp contrast to the two deputy carabinieri who had continued to follow and watch.

Thus Alfonso was launched on a week-long excursion into the depths of time that would reshape his consideration of his place in the world. Riccardo took Alfonso to the Pistoia estate of the late Dr. Francesco Chiappelli who had been a well-regarded Pistoian physician; after the death of their father in 1888, his three sons had converted the estate into a residential research center. The brothers—Alberto, Luigi, and Alessandro—had joined with other learned professionals to form the Pistoia Historical Society; the converted Chiappelli estate now was an extension of the local university, serving as a library for an extensive collection of historical books and documents, as a museum for ancient artifacts, and as a gathering place for intellectual discourse.

Alfonso was provided with a suite of rooms, a place to bathe and clean up, and a modest selection of clothes. He had acquired a shirt and cap to 'civilianize' his wardrobe, completed with U.S. Army trousers, boots, and undergarments. Riccardo later admitted that the clothes were his own, as he had guessed that they would have been about the same size. On the train ride to Pistoia, Riccardo had explained to Alfonso that the brothers had an engaging intellectual curiosity. Upon hearing that Alfonso was coming to the region, the brothers had sent for Riccardo and dispatched him with an invitation to be their guest. "The Senator in particular wants to speak to you about the social development of America and American politics."

Their gesture was not entirely benevolent, Riccardo explained. The brothers were active in the political and civil life of the city and region. Luigi Chiappelli, a lawyer, previously served on the municipal council for Pistoia and currently was on the provincial council of Florence. Dr. Alessandro Chiappelli was a Senator for the Kingdom of Italy, having attained that post in 1914. The brothers were staunch supporters of the Catholic tradition and their politics were linked to moderate liberal Catholicism. Their oldest brother, Dr. Alberto Chiappelli, previously had served on the Pistoia council. The brothers were members of the Democratic Liberal party. It was specific to their political interests that Alfonso had been invited to this gathering.

Their political party had been opposed to Italian entry into the war, supporting the call for peace from the Catholic pope Benedict XV. They wanted to publicly embrace a family member who had participated in the war in order to soften their earlier pacifist message and appeal to the more aggressive wing that was emerging within their own party. Alfonso could return on the morning train back to Granaglione without getting involved, or he could stay on and enjoy a feast held in his honor.

Without ever agreeing to the arrangements, Alfonso was caught up in a whirlwind of activities that stimulated his imagination and kept him fully occupied for the remaining days of his leave. He never had a moment to say no. When he opened the door from his sleeping quarters the next morning he was met by Dr. Alberto Chiappelli, the oldest of the brothers (each of whom had reached their 60th year in age) who, along with Riccardo, provided a tour of the research center, mixed with meals and meetings.

Each of the brothers was distinguished in his own right. In addition to being a well-regarded physician, Dr. Alberto Chiappelli was well versed in the medical practices of the ancient Romans and their earlier predecessors, the Etruscans. He published studies on the sanitary regulations in Pistoia during the black plague of 1348 and noted that through epidemiology analysis he was able to show that many Etruscan descendants, including members of the Chiappelli family, had acquired immunity from the plague due to exposure to the disease a thousand years earlier when they lived in Anatolia, a region of Asia Minor.

Alberto could barely contain his enthusiasm in sharing with Alfonso and Riccardo, an Etruscan funerary vase that was recovered from under the sand and mud of a lagoon that was drained of its brackish water near the city of Ravenna on the east coast of the Italian Peninsula. It was near that location that the first Etruscans had settled, Alberto explained. The funeral urn contained the remains of Kuranta Chia who the Chiappelli brothers claimed was an ancient forbearer in the Chiappelli family.

Alberto continued his lecture by describing the system of hydraulics that the Etruscans had employed to drain marshlands and create a water canal that connected the Adriatic Sea on the east coast of Italy via a waterway running through the center of the peninsula to Rome and the Tyrrhenian Sea on the west coast. This knowledge of hydraulic engineering was put to good use in regulating river flows, in preventing the silting up of harbors, and in providing a complex system of reticulated water for public use. Water was reticulated by means of underground water pipes and pressure boxes, a technology that was not passed on to the Romans.

"We are all things Chia," Luigi Chiappelli, esquire, opined when he joined the entourage later that day. In addition to his law practice, Luigi was a professor of history specializing in Italian law, and a highly regarded student of local Pistoia history, family structure, and genealogy. He pointed to engravings on the funeral urn that represented grapes used in Chianti wine; other drawings depicted the Chianina cattle that early family members had processed through tanneries to provide the quality leather through which Pistoia had built its reputation in the footwear industry. The Etruscans were masters of metallurgy and even practiced dentistry.

Luigi spoke with expression and none-stop in explaining the family history, quickly noting that although they shared the Chiappelli name, their relationship was that of 10th cousins, twice removed. He explained how he had traced the family origin. "Last names for other than royalty were not adopted in Europe until the 14th century. Recordkeeping by the Catholic church was mandated by the Council of Trent in 1560 and it is rare to find last-name records predating that time." He showed Alfonso and Riccardo documents preserved from the census of 1244 that listed 18 hearths at Chiappore on the Val di Bura river. "It is from that grouping of hovels that the Chiappelli emerged," Luigi concluded.

The family was devoted in its fealty to the Catholic Church, Alberto stated with pride as he reported that the Chiappore had built a massive chapel at the top of a mountain that stood like a beacon to God in the midst of the clouds. The chapel also provided strategic observation of the entire area, which helped the Chiappore control passage through the mountain strongholds. In this manner the family came to the attention of the House of Savoy who singled out Ulvieri for distinction; he was added to their Order of Saint Maurice and Lazarus, and henceforth the family was called Chiappelli; reduced to English, the name would be Chappell or chapel. That was back in the 15th century, about the year 1470.

The House of Savoy is the oldest royal dynasty in Europe, having been established in 1003 when Humberto, Count of Sabaudia, was assigned control of the region of Savoy in the Alpine region between what is now France and Italy, Luigi explained. Over time, the House of Savoy expanded its territory and influence; from rule of a small region on the French/Italian border, the dynasty's realm grew to include nearly all of the Italian Peninsula through judicious marriages and international diplomacy, and, of course, control over strategic mountain passes in the Alps.

"You are a direct descendant from Ulivieri," Luigi explained, "whereas my brothers and I are descended from Caldone Chiappelli, a brother to Ulivieri."

"You have another distinction in your line," Senator Alessandro Chiappelli said in joining the conversation. "Guerrino Chiappelli was your 9th great-grandfather."

"Who was he?" Alfonso asked, confessing that he had never heard the name before. "Do you not know your Tuscan history?" Alessandro responded with exaggerated surprise. "Guerrino fought gallantly in the Battle of Gavinana," he began explaining in detail, the next in the number of lectures that Alfonso would enjoy as the day wore on.

Riccardo maintained his company with Alfonso, and for the first time since meeting in Granaglione they found themselves alone. Alfonso used the opportunity to ask about Riccardo's family and his father, the Conti.

"My father died several months ago," Riccardo blurted out as tears formed in his eyes.

"I am so sorry," Alfonso immediately offered, recognizing in the next instant, "…so that would make you the Count." From the tensed response of Riccardo, Alfonso knew he had struck a chord. He also recognized his poor manners in not having asked sooner about the Conti.

"That is not a popular position to hold these days," Riccardo said. He felt personally responsible for the economic stability of the estate entrusted to the management of the Conti Chiappelli. "Expectations far exceed resources. We are in deep trouble. A village of families depends on me."

"Perhaps your father should return to the Villa di Cireglio to take charge. He could be the Conti."

"That is not possible," Alfonso quickly stated, thinking about the ugly scene when he visited with his Uncle Umberto.

"Actually, it could be possible. There is more family history that you should want to know," Riccardo began. "It has to do with your grandfather, Carlo Ferrando Chiappelli. He should have inherited the title and position of Conti Chiappelli, not my father. And that would have placed your father Egisto next in line to receive the title.

Alfonso was stunned; not because of the announcement, but moreso because of the importance Riccardo was attributing to the scenario. "I did not know my grandfather was in line to be considered," Alfonso responded.

"He was and he was not," Riccardo said. "It is complicated. I will try to explain.

"The affiliation with the House of Savoy did not come from our paternal line; it came from the maternal side of our family. As you know, your grandfather Carlo Ferrando and my father Giuseppe Giovanni were brothers; their grandfather Giovanni Battista Chiappelli was the Conti. Giovanni Battista received the title through his mother who was born Bartolomea Chiappelli, daughter of the Conti Giovanni Piero. Two Chiappelli branches that had sprung from the Ulivieri merged with the marriage of Bernardo Chiappelli and Bartolomea Chiappelli.

"The title then went to an uncle to Carlo Ferrando and Giuseppe Giovanni. This uncle did not have any children, but he did have several nephews to consider for the position, several who became his namesake; his name was Carlo.

"My father was selected for Conti over your grandfather because your Carlo Ferrando supported the social revolution of Garibaldi, which was counter to the House of Savoy, a position that later was reversed. The Catholic bishop supported this decision."

"Was there not another branch of the family to consider for the title?" Alfonso asked.

"Yes. There was another nephew, also named Carlo, but he had no sons. That is why our branch was chosen."

"So why are you telling me this now?" Alfonso asked after Riccardo had paused for an extended time, in the same instance thinking that this could be the reason why his father Egisto had such a distrust of the church.

In a rush of words, Riccardo laid out details of an unsettled country. He felt threatened physically, emotionally, and financially. Mostly, he said, he felt alone. Riccardo talked and Alfonso listened; options were listed, weighing pros and cons of all possible actions. Riccardo even suggested that Alfonso and his family could return to Tuscany to help manage the estate. Your father could be the Conti, Riccardo said. In a moment of selfishness Alfonso imagined that such a scenario could happen; more quickly he came to his senses and recognized that perhaps Riccardo was overthinking his plight.

"Your real work is just starting," Alfonso said, repeating what BGen. Hearn had announced to his men, "and the most that you can do is the least that is expected of you."

"You worry too much about others," Alfonso counseled. "Take my advice. Look after yourself first; if you are not stable, you will not be available to help others. The details will work themselves forward; they always do."

"The brothers said pretty much the same thing," Riccardo admitted. "I just want you to know that you are always welcome to come back."

"It is not easy being a Chiappelli," Alfonso mingled into the buona sera.

chapter twelve

Each of the brothers quizzed Alfonso extensively during the days of his stay, asking questions about every aspect of life in America and his emigration. Even when he confessed that he knew little about the American political system, the brothers continued to press for information and Alfonso shared all the details about his maturing in America. The senator, in particular, asked probing questions about American freedoms, social liberties, and self-expression. "Pistoians have a storied history in fighting for the right to self-govern," Luigi explained, noting that the Tuscan city of Pistoia was the first commune to establish governance by the people."

"In 1105 the city was ruled by consuls," Luigi explained, "the most ancient form of democratic magistracy; in 1158 the Podesta (governor) curbed the power of the Catholic bishop and in 1177 the city of Pistoia passed its first statute, one of the oldest in Italy. During the next two centuries, Pistoia grew in economic strength and expanded its influence over a large territory that brought it into conflict with other city-states. This eventually led to her downfall."

"The internal strife in Pistoia only made matters worse," Alberto interrupted. He explained that different political factions had emerged with such divisiveness that the city could no longer stand on its own.

"Of course they were fighting for control over the economic wealth," Alberto stated. By the middle of the 13th century, he explained, northern Italy was a myriad of more than 60 independent city-states, not counting smaller villages that claimed liberties backed up by larger cities. The Papalcy ruled over Central Italy. The game of power made every northern Italian town a theater of civil wars. It was a time of unmitigated violence; entire families were expunged in escalating blood feuds. Two major groups coalesced in 1198—the Guelphs who became the upholders of papal supremacy, and the Ghibellines who supported political claims of German emperors and the aristocracy. The names were German in origin.

"These factions steadily degenerated into gangs without any ideology who fought for the ambitions of their own bosses to control local businesses and rackets," Luigi lectured. By the end of the 13th century, opposition to the Ghibellines virtually ended their influence in Italy. This violent resistance was replaced by a split within the Guelph party; Neri (Black) Guelphs became a faction of the upper middle class, with the Bianchi (White) Guelphs the faction of the lower middle class.

In May 1305, an army of 21,000 infantrymen and 4,000 cavalry of the Black party were sent from Florence and Lucca to subdue the White faction that held Pistoia. Although they were drastically outnumbered, the Pistoians held through the strength of their walls and resisted for 11 months in the hope that allies would rally to their cause. Help never came, nor was it ever sent. Famine began to reduce the number of defenders and by April 1306 further resistance was futile. Pistoia fell under the influence of Florence and if ever there was a chance of restoring her independence, it was removed by disastrous plagues of 1348 and 1400 in which more than half of the city population perished.

"Pistoians lost their status as an independent city-state but continued to enjoy individual liberties enabled by the *res publica* influence of Florence," Luigi continued. "This freedom lasted for another two centuries until the liberties of a Republic ended for all Tuscans on 3 August 1530 at the Battle of Gavinana," Luigi Chiappelli concluded. He quoted historian, J.A. Symonde to make his point:

"From 1530 to 1796, that is, for a period of nearly three centuries, the Italians had no history of their own. Their annals are
filled with records of dynastic changes and redistributions of
territory, consequent upon treaties signed by foreign powers,
in the settlement of quarrels which nowise concerned the
people. Italy only too often became the theatre of desolating
and distracting wars. But these wars were fought for the most
part by alien armies; the points at issue were decided beyond
the Alps; the gains accrued to royal families whose names
were unpronounceable by southern tongues. That the Italians
had created modern civilization for Europe availed them
nothing. Italy, intellectually first among the peoples, was now
politically and practically last; and nothing to her historian
is more heart-rendering than to watch gradual extinction of
her spirit in this age of slavery."

"The Etruscans must have felt the same way," Alberto added to
the conversation, giving introduction to a topic he would return
to frequently.

The senator Alessandro used the interruption to return to his
lecture on the Battle of Gavinana:

"In 1527 the French monarch ordered his army to occupy
territories of the duke of Savoy, directly challenging the Catholic
Church for control of the Italian peninsula. On 26 April 1527, the
Bourbon army reached the walls of Florence; control of the city had
been lost to powers of the pope in 1512. On this day the cardinal
who commanded for the pope distributed arms among the citizens
for their defense. The city held, but Rome did not. The Florence
citizenry on 17 May restored the grand council to governance of
their city, and Tuscans again declared their independence. It was
readily apparent that the city would need to build a military force
in order to maintain her liberty. Machiavelli, who died on 22 June
1527, long had been engaged in persuading his fellow citizens of
the necessity of awakening a military spirit in the people; it was he

who caused the country militia, named *l'ordinanza*, to be formed into regiments; Guerrino Chiappelli was in that number. A body of mercenaries organized by Giovanni de Medici earned distinction as the *bande nere*.

"Within the city, Florentines formed two bodies of militia. The first, consisting of 300 men from noble families, undertook the guard of the palace; the second, 4,000 soldiers drawn from among the families who had a right to sit in the council-general, were called the civic militia. The illustrious Michaelangelo was charged to superintend the fortifications of Florence. This construction was completed in April 1529, just in time to meet an onslaught from the oppressors, led by the Prince of Orange, who had been sent to regain the city for the pope. The prince encamped his army in the plain of Ripoli at the foot of the walls of Florence. By December this army was joined by 20,000 Spaniards and Germans who occupied, without resistance, the territories and cities of Pistoia and Prato.

The solitary chance Florentines had for deliverance was in command of Francesco Ferrucci who had learned the art of war in the bande nere. He had been named commissary general and was at this time working outside the city gathering provisions. Learning of the peril that threatened the city, Ferrucci traversed Tuscany and gathered in the mountains of Pistoia every man of courage still devoted to the republic. One of these troops was Guerrino Chiappelli who had participated in the l'ordinanza.

During those summer months, Ferrucci gathered 1,300 harquebusiers, 1,000 pikemen, 300 other infantry with swords, halberds and partisans, and four squadrons of lance spezzate and cavalry; they were recognizable for the white bands that they wore. From 14 July to 2 August 1530, Ferrucci led his troops through the Apennine Mountains with numerous bodies of the opposing imperialists preceding, following, and surrounding him on all sides. When Ferrucci led his force of 3,000 infantry and 500 cavalry into the mountain village of Gavinana, a little town near Pistoia on top of a hill between two rivers, at mid-day on 3 August 1530, the prince of Orange was at the same time moving into the hamlet from the opposite direction.

"All shit let loose," Riccardo laughed. He had heard the story before; Guerrino Chiappelli was his 9th great-grandfather also.

"Yes, the fighting was fierce," the senator continued after casting a frown at Riccardo. "Ferrucci, on a white horse, led his vanguard with baggage train in the middle. He had a dozen mortars at his disposal and 20 trombe artifiziate, weapons that were like a flame-thrower. The Florentine force, although spread thin by the necessity of having to protect against attacks from all sides, repelled the fighting corps of the Prince of Orange who was killed by a double shot from a harquebusier. The imperialists, recognizable for their red bands, had entered the village with about 1,000 troops. The success of the Florentines was short lived, as 8,000 imperialist rein-forcements arrived to add strength to the enemy army on all sides. Francesco Ferrucci, pierced with several mortal wounds, dropped to the ground from exhaustion and was taken prisoner, along with Guerrino Chiappelli and others who had fought at his side. Guer-rino, also severely wounded, reported that the enemy commander Fabrizio Maramaldi, a Calabrese who had taken command after the death of the Prince of Orange, upon entering the room where they were being held assaulted Ferrucci in a rage. His report concluded that Ferrucci had laughed at his enemy while he was being stabbed, and said "you are killing a dead man."

When news of this defeat reached Florence, the city leaders negotiated surrender terms, which included payment of 80,000 crowns to the army and recall of the Medici to governance. In return, a complete amnesty was to be granted to all who had acted against the pope, the Medici family, or the French emperor. The pope responded with different terms and directed that captured militia be imprisoned, tortured and killed; Guerrino Chiappelli was among the 150 citizens who suffered this fate that September of 1530; before the end of the year every Florentine family of distinction including those devoted to the Medici had a family member listed among the 1,000 so proscribed.

"Now you understand," the senator concluded, "that we Tuscans have a long history of fighting for civil liberties. The quest for that individual freedom must have influenced your decision to emigrate to the United States," Alessandro said rhetorically. Alfonso responded that he had moved to America at age 8. The senator nodded, of course, and shifted the discussion to politics. He quizzed Alfonso extensively on the planned construction of the coal towns, the relationship between the workers and the mine owners, the commerce, and the interaction of the immigrations from different countries.

The senator explained that after the war, Italy had received an area contested with Slovenia that soon would be asked to elect a representative. The Trentino-Alto region had been the scene of fierce fighting between the Italians and Slovenes. The Slovene military had fought and won 12 major engagements in what they called the "Soška fronta;" although they had won every battle in the area Italians call Isonzo, they lost the war. Now they were being asked to help the Italians govern their region.

Earlier in his professional career, Senator Chiappelli had been a professor a History of Philosophy at the University of Naples. His works *The Philosophical Premises of Socialism* and *Socialism and Modern Thought* often were cited in justifications for the fascist movement. This was a concern to Senator Chiappelli as he examined the politics of his day.

Italy was a nation built on compromise, he explained. In its short history (Italy did not merge as a kingdom until 1861), a single political party has never held a majority. So it becomes necessary to form a coalition with others with whom you often disagree.

Italy was in the midst of the *Biennio Rosso,* a revolutionary period marked by violence introduced by blackshirts representing themselves as fascist militia. Immediately after the end of the war, the senator explained, massive strikes often led by returning soldiers were creating an economic crisis. Two groups particularly drawn to fascism were war veterans unable to find good jobs and discontented by the peace terms Italy had won, and the lower middle class, hard hit by inflation and chronic unemployment.

"We are trying to work with them," Luigi said. Although he was somewhat skeptical about the outcome, he explained that his intellectual curiosity had overcome his resistance to what he called experiments in self-management. Worker councils had been formed and many factory and farms occupations took place under their leadership. "Mussolini is promising change, by violent means if necessary, and presenting fascists as a superpatriotic band of idealists which alone can save Italy." Concern showed through the worry lines that creased the face of each Chiappelli.

The Democratic Liberal party was inspired by Catholic social teaching. Its platform called for an elective Senate, proportional representation, corporatism, agrarian reform, women's suffrage, political decentralization, independence of the Catholic Church, and social legislation. The party was able to claim 252 out of 508 seats, but its coalition quickly was splitting apart between pro- and anti-fascist elements. Although he did not embrace fascism, Senator Chiappelli explained, he felt it necessary to hold onto his senate seat in the coalition in order to maintain a voice in the chamber. "It is an opportunity to introduce intellectual reasoning into the conversation," Alessandro said, adding wishfully, "Sometimes it works."

———— ❧ ————

A DARK AND DREARY DAY DID NOT DAMPEN THE ENTHUSIASM of the Chiappelli entourage as they set out the next day on an escorted tour of Pistoia. They began at the local hospital where their host, introduced only as the administrator, alerted the group that they would see parts of Pistoia that only a privileged few had been fortunate to inspect. She shared details from a prepared script:

"The hospital became a civic project that provides architectural evidence of one of the oldest hospital structures in the world still in use today. The project began in 1277 and was financed by a deeply religious couple. It was an established custom to place alms in a hollow trunk at the gates of religious orders; through their meditative reflection on giving, this couple envisioned a place where they would find a trunk flowering in the dead of winter and at that site they would establish a ministry for care to all who present themselves. This hollow trunk is called a 'ceppo,' thus the beginning of the Ospedale del Ceppo.

"The original hospital wards of the Ospedale del Ceppo were structures that extended from the Church of Saint Maria. A renovation planned in 1502 copied the architectural design that noted Italian architect Filippo Brunelleschi had used in 1419 in the construction of the Ospedale del Innocenti in Florence, providing an arched colonnade for the entrance."

Dr. Alberto Chiappelli joined the conversation by noting "The same design, often cited as the launch of Renaissance construction, was informed by architectural techniques learned from Etruscan examples for building pillars and arches. We will see such an example later in our tour."

The hospital administrator nodded agreement and continued:

"A primary contributor to the Pistoia project was Giovanni della Robbia whose glazed terracotta sculpture frieze is considered the greatest work of the della Robbia family. Andrea della Robbia, father of Giovanni, provided the sculptural details in working with Brunelleschi on that Florence hospital.

"The story of the recovery from the plague is told in the polychrome frieze over the portico that was commissioned to promote the hospital's charitable goals. Religious and civic organizations were overwhelmed with bequeaths of estates and donations in the aftermath of the Black Plague and the Ospedale del Ceppo was no exception. In fact, it had so much money that the Ospedale became the object of bitter fighting between opposing factions of the Panciatichi (Bianchi) and Cancellieri (Neri) families. The polychrome decoration was commissioned in 1526 and completed in 1528. There are seven panels, one at each end of the colonnade and above each of the five columns. The seven panels represent works of charity:

* dressing the unclothed,

* assisting widows,

* sheltering pilgrims,

* helping the infirmed,

* visiting the imprisoned,

* burying the dead,

* feeding the hungry,

* giving drink to the thirsty.

"The scenes are divided by vertical reliefs of decorated pilasters that frame allegorical figures representing the virtues— prudence, faith, charity, hope, justice. In the corners are two imaginary figures with the symbol of the ceppo at their feet."

"Inspiration for a health facility is drawn from a calling to the ministry of health; it is a symbol of caring; not just the care of the individual physical body but caring for the spirit of people as they unite in a social community. The Ospedale del Ceppo is an example of this ministry and reflects the social evolution of Pistoia."

She drew applause when in closing she pointed out a caricature intended to portray Leonardo Buonafede who commissioned the work on behalf of Florentine management. He was my 7th great-grandfather she said, holding back a smile as she introduced herself: Dr. Lisa Buonafede.

Luigi Chiappelli added details: "The Pistoia region in the 13th and 14th centuries was populated with 34,000 countrymen who labored in vineyards and olive groves in the foothills of the Apennines or maintained herds of goat and sheep in mountain enclaves. The population within the city gates numbered 11,000. This population count held constant until the Black Plague devastated the region in 1348 and again in 1398-99. The census in the year 1400 found a population reduced by 74% in the countryside and 44.5% in the city. Among those 9,000 survivors in the country and 6,000 fortunates within the city walls, walked members of the Chiappelli family."

Lisa Buonafede pointed to a preserved copy of the *"Ordinances for Sanitation in a Time of Mortality,"* which became model legislation for cities controlling the disease when it was issued in 1348 by the city council of Pistoia. The public health directive essentially quarantined the city, established specific monetary penalties for non-compliance, and established authority for enforcement with these provisions:

1. no Pistoian citizen shall in any way dare to presume to go to Pisa or Lucca or outlying districts,

2. forbidden to bring into the district or city any used cloth, either linen or woolen, for use as clothing or bedclothes,

3. bodies of dead must be removed from place where they are found in a wooden casket covered by a lid and secured with nails so that no stench can issue forth,

4. in order to avoid foul stench any ditch in which a dead body is buried must be at least 2 ½ braccia (approximately 6 feet),

5. no dead bodies shall be brought into the city, whether in or out of a casket, and gatekeepers who permit entry shall be equally fined,

6. no person who attends the funeral shall be permitted to be in the presence of the body or to enter the home of the deceased, nor may they be in the presence of relatives except in the funeral procession,

7. no gifts before or after the funeral shall be sent to the home of the deceased nor shall meals be attended, except for immediate family,

8. no person shall presume to dress in new clothing for an eight-day period of mourning, with an exception for the wife of the deceased,

9. no paid mourners,

10. no sounding of bells with the exception of a single ring at a church or chapel where a burial is being conducted,

11. no gatherings for purpose of evicting widows from their homes, with an exception for no more than four women who are blood relatives who are permitted to accompany the widow,

12. no speaking of the dead; no wailing or clamor over any person or because of any person who has died outside the district, no gatherings, no bells rung, no announcements, nor any invitation to talk about deaths outside the district,

13. (number not used)

14. butchers and retail vendors of meat are forbidden to hang or store any meat that gives off a putrid smell or any stench,

15. stench and putrefaction being harmful to man, tanning of hides is forbidden within the city walls,

16. the Lord Podesta, Captain, and officials charged pro tem, shall proceed against, investigate, and inquire…all infractions, and assign and collect fines. Any person who accuses another shall tender one-fourth of the potential fine to be forfeited if the charge is unfounded.

"It would seem that the public health surveillance was largely an issue of smell," Alfonso said after reading the list, drawing a round of laughter that would be repeated throughout the day.

The featured part of the tour came when the entourage was led to a hypogeum—an underground river—that ran beneath the hospital. "This is the example of Etruscan know-how that was mentioned before," Alberto said. "Note the stone archway entrance. The pillars used in this and other public works comply with defined ratios that engineers say are an improvement over the Corinthian, Doric, and Ionian supports found in Greek-influenced structures."

Buonafede explained that the stone archway opened to a water canal 700 meters long (3,000 feet), half of which lies beneath the Ospedale del Ceppo. The original construction reflects medical support logical for a medieval fort, she explained, noting that it provided access to a large open ward enclosure near the line of defense. Archeologists sponsored by the Pistoia Historical Society were recovering the underground path, she noted, giving nodding credit to the Chiappelli brothers.

"The use of the hypogeum is part of that lost knowledge that we are trying to recover from the Etruscans," Alberto noted.

Buonafede returned to her talking points.

"Pistoia became a defensive stronghold and seat of a 'castaldia' under the Lombards, beginning in the 6th century. Defensive walls were built in an articulated double ring separated by a walkway for the guards; the walls were six meters (almost 20 feet) thick at the base and about 14 meters (46 feet) high. Prior to this construction, the site served as a Roman outpost and preceding that land use there is evidence of an Etruscan settlement. The hypogeum established self-sufficiency for the site as a fortification, with access to a protected water source located inside of the city walls. This artificial water canal also served as a mill race, marking urban activities of a pre-industrial city, with the water used to power a waterwheel which in turn powered grist mills."

The entourage concluded its tour for the day with a return to the research center where they were greeted by Francesco Chiappelli, son of the lawyer Luigi. Francesco was about five years older than Alfonso. He was a professor of art history and had just that day returned from his studio in Florence.

"His fame is spreading," Luigi boasted of his son, "through his creative use of lithography." Francesco beamed at his father's compliment, but said little.

Throughout the evening meal, Alfonso repeatedly caught Francesco staring at him. When he showed his discomfort in returning the stare, Francesco smiled and Riccardo chuckled. "He wants to draw your portrait," Riccardo explained. The next morning Francesco did exactly that, creating a charcoal likeness of Alfonso that easily could be mistaken for a photographic image.

The whirlwind continued over the next days as the brothers took turns leading Alfonso to sites through the city, introducing him to civic leaders, businessmen, politicians, clergy, and others in authority as "my cousin, the American soldier." Indeed, each day increased the feeling Alfonso had that he was valued as a member of the family.

The brothers led him to the Duomo square of Pistoia, framed by ancient and beautiful buildings, monuments and churches. They toured the Cathedral and its Belfry, the Baptistery, the Town Hall, the Tribunal, and the old Bishop's Palace. The Cathedral dates back to the 5th century and has been reconstructed several times. The façade, in Romanesque style, has three rows of loggias and a portico in marble decorated with Della Robbia terracotta. Inside the Cathedral were the sepulchral monument of the 14th century poet Cino da Pistoia, excellent paintings and frescoes, and a splendid silver altar dedicated to the patron saint of the city, Saint Jacopo.

Never at a loss to note, Alberto added, "The masterly embossment of the altar panels as well as the use of precious stones and refined enamel elements all are proof of the high artistic level reached by Tuscan gold and silversmiths who were influenced by their Etruscan heritage."

Another splendid example, this one designed by noted designer Giovanni Pisano, was the pulpit at the Church of Saint Andrea. Inside the town hall they visited the Civic Museum and the Michelucci Centre, dedicated to this architect who was born in Pistoia and who had designed many of the buildings. Alfonso was particularly impressed with the white and green marble façade on a church designed by Michaelangelo, a style repeated in Florence.

Senator Alessandro took special pride in showing Alfonso the well of Leoncino which was being restored by the Historical Society. The lintel had three bands; on the right decorated in white marble, the coat of arms of the city craftsmen; the Florentine lily at the center; and the Pistoia coat of arms to the left.

Alfonso was treated to a front row center seat in the soccer stadium where the local sports collective competed with a team from Florence in "the historic game of Calcio in Costume." Soccer—calico in Italian—was a popular activity in military encampments to keep the men physically fit for combat. During the siege of Florence in 1530, Michaelangelo, a self-described Etruscan said Alberto, arranged for teams to play soccer in costumes to keep up the ancient tradition of playing games during carnival and to show scorn for the besieging troops. The words *Poveri ma Liberi* (poor but free) were found scrawled on walls. To emphasize the scorn, a group of Florentine musicians played from the roof of a nearby church.

"A subtle reminder that we continue the fight for individual liberty," Luigi concluded. He noted that "calcio storico" is still played today and followed fervently by Pistoians prideful of their history.

chapter thirteen

The last evening of his stay in Pistoia, Alfonso again was seated center stage at a feast held in his honor and sponsored by the Pistoia Historical Society. The meal was organized and prepared at the direction of highly regarded chef Elaine Trigiani. Prior to the banquet, Trigiani shared with Alfonso details of the meal preparation. Beginning as a child, Alfonso had always watched with interest the respect his mother had shown for the ingredients she used in her food. The menu was impressive, especially for these post-war days.

- crostini neri (chicken liver and cow spleen)
- kale crostini
- chestnut flour pasta with caramelized onions and herbs
- spit roasted rabbit, squab and chicken
- boiled cabbage and broccoli rabe ('i rapi)
- castagnaccio
- red wine, vin santo

Signora Trigiani pointed to the 'animale di cortile' and explained with pride how she was able to barter for the rabbit, squab and chicken that were spit-roasted with bay leaves that are prevalent in Tuscany, and basted with the fat.

"This light pink flour ground from chestnuts—called "farina dolce" or sweet flour because it actually does taste slightly sweet—was used to make the bread. It is quite tasty with a piece of young, sharp sheep milk cheese.

"We used farina dolce to make the bread and pasta because we do not have any wheat," she explained. "Because of the war, all the farmers were out fighting, and no one cultivated any of the wheat. We call the bread "pan di legno"—wooden bread—because it is so heavy due to the flour we have to use."

Chef Trigiani explained that the pasta was made from chestnut flour, served with caramelized onions, walnuts and wild herbs. Chestnut flour is a dusty pink when it's dry, and then turns mahogany brown when mixed with liquid. Trigiani demonstrated for Alfonso how flour was made from dried chestnuts.

"To dry chestnuts they are put in the upper level of a seccatoio (smoke house) and a fire is maintained on the ground floor for 2 months or so," she explained, "providing perpetual coals for grilling if you are lucky enough to have a piece of meat, or a radicchio. When the chestnuts are dry and hard as little rocks they are shelled by stomping on them wearing clogs with spikes and then the nutmeats are hand sorted from the shells. Then the rock hard chestnuts—kids suck on them as if they were candy—are toasted again in a bread oven, and then milled into flour by the ancient miller down at the water-powered mill along the river. Just hauling the sacks of chestnuts down to the mill and then the sacks of flour back up to the village was a large chore."

Trigiani said she also had bartered with some of the local women who kept vegetable gardens for cavolo nero (black cabbage) which she had boiled and finely chopped and then cooked with some vinegar and added to boiled broccoli rabe, 'i rapi, sautéed with garlic and olive oil. She topped a thin piece of pan di legno with a spread made with chicken livers, sage and a splash of vin santo. Wine and olive oil were pulled from the dwindling stock in the cellar.

Alfonso was well aware of the Tuscany treat "castagnaccio," made with a soupy mix of chestnut flour, water, olive oil, rosemary, raisins, and pine nuts or walnuts. Although Alfonso enjoyed it most as an appetizer, his mother often had offered the treat as a dessert. The ingredients are mixed and placed into a shallow pan, slid into a hot oven and cooked until the mixture dries out and little cracks form on the top.

"It tastes best with a glass of red wine as an appetizer," he said, offering the opinion that castagnaccio is not for dessert because it is decidedly not sweet enough.

DR. ALBERTO CHIAPPELLI, THE FEATURED SPEAKER, PROVIDED an informative lecture on "the Sea People of Italy."

"All Tuscans should know this story," Alberto began. "The Etruscans were Sea People. The anthropology of the Sea Peoples explains many of the mysteries and legends that fall within the cracks of recorded history. The victors gain not only the spoils of conquest but also control over how history records their use of those resources. This explains the misrepresentation of the Sea Peoples in written records and misunderstanding of those who interpret those records.

"The Sea Peoples were at heart a peaceful tribe of families. Their way of life was one of exchanging goods and services, knowledge and ideas. With no doubt they were skillful warriors who would fight in viscous defense of their people. This is told in stories throughout the lands where they had made their presence known. Therein lies the problem; the stories are plentiful as the Sea Peoples and they were known in a lot of places by a lot of different names. The transient nature and ability of the Sea Peoples further challenges the historical record, as the advancement of their culture must have made them appear as gods to some, or monsters to others, to the primitive people they encountered.

"The social advancement of the Sea Peoples can be attributed in part to the comfort of a stable food supply and resources for shelter and clothing; thus, they had time to think in a period of time when most of the remaining world population was focused on simple survival. Combine this with a fierce independence matched only with generosity of spirit, the result is an individual freedom that might happen only once in this earth time.

"There is no doubt that the Chiappelli were affiliated with the Sea Peoples; it fell upon a single ancestor in time to be nurtured across the waters to the Italian Peninsula. Although the migration can be traced to a single individual in the Chiappelli chain, this move involved entire families benefiting from generations of planning.

"The worldwide population in 1200BC was about 100 million. Approximately 2.5 million Sea Peoples populated the shorelines of the Mediterranean and Aegean seas; included in this number were about 200,000 members of the Rasenna, living in 200 coastal settlements in an area of Asia Minor now known as western Turkey, with an average population of 10,000.

"They called themselves the 'Rasenna' which roughly translated means the collective voice of the people. The 'speaker of the people's voice' was called the 'Ruba,' an elected position that was rotated every year among the family leaders—an example of leadership later adopted by the Romans. The enigma of the Rasenna is not that its records have been lost to time, but rather that the ability to understand those records has given way to the eternal dust. The Rasenna were among the first to recognize individual liberties in a free society. Women had equal status as men. Every prisoner had the chance to earn their freedom after a period of apprenticeship.

"The Rasenna were an intellectually advanced people in a primitive world. Consequently much of the historical record from other civilizations in that time period records advanced knowledge of nature as mystical relationships to gods. Likewise, advanced understanding of science was translated to augury.

"The Rasenna would examine the livers of animals to gain an insight into the cyclical processing of that spirit in this world. In much the same way that the length of winter can be predicted by the width of the black ring on the wooly worm, the texture, color and smell of a liver spoke volumes to the Rasenna. The primitive people who observed the Rasenna would have assigned religious pretense to most of that which they could not understand. What would appear to be a list of gods to those primitive souls would be nothing more than a list of major courses of study at a university for the Rasenna. Dogma creeps into the unknown and feeds the greed of the ignorant.

"A catastrophic event occurred in the year 1320BC that shattered the advance of this civilization, forever changing the Rasenna—Mount Sipylus was hit by a meteor. The resulting earthquake shook the mountain into the Lake Saloe, flooding the entire valley, and swamped the kingdom of King Tantalos. The Chia compound was devastated and the living quarters were uninhabitable. The family rounded up what cattle it could find, loaded wagons with whatever goods they could salvage, and moved to Ahhiyawa, known today as Lydia.

"There was a mass migration of populations during this period in time. Climate changes and famines were the product of volcanic eruptions, meteor showers, and earthquakes, resulting in fires and tsunamis. The invasions were not merely military operations, but involved the movements of large populations by land and sea seeking new lands to settle. Long periods of drought, and resulting famine, created the socio-economic incentive for war. Mid-winter storms from the Atlantic Ocean were diverted to travel north of the Pyreees and the Alps, bringing wetter conditions to Central Europe, but drought to the Eastern Mediterranean. Paleoclimatologian research has confirmed these climatic conditions.

A passage from the historian Herodotus explains what happened next:

"In the days of Atys, the son of Manes, there was a great scarcity through the whole land…so the king determined to divide the nation in half…the one to stay, the other to leave the land…the emigrants should have his son Tyrrhenus for their leader…they went down to Smyrna and built themselves ships…after sailing past many countries they came to Umbria …and called themselves…Tyrrhenians."

"This planned migration for half of the surviving Rasenna population began about the year 1200BC. To this day a Chiappelli can return to Lydia and find someone descended from a brother of our forbearer, the brother who remained behind. They will know they have arrived at their ancestral home because a full-faced image is sculptured in rock at Mount Spil; called the 'weeping rock,' the carved image serves as a permanent lookout for those who sailed away.

"They were called 'tuscii' in Latin. The obvious explanation for this has always been their fondness for building tower-like, walled, hilltop towns like those still to be seen scattered across Tuscany. The Villa di Cireglio is our family example, as is her twin villa, Saturnana. The people now known as Etruscans were a fun loving and eclectic people who among other things taught the French how to make wine, the Romans how to build roads, and all of Europe how to write and count. What are widely known as Roman numerals was a numbering system provided by the Etruscans.

"The greatly reduced population of the Etruscans led them to coalesce with the Latin population; this powerful influence on organization and planning provided the foundation for the building of the Roman empire. This influence can be identified in all aspects of Tuscan life. For example, the most common head wear of Etruscans was a conical-type woolen hat still worn to this day by Tuscan farmers."

At this point in the lecture, Alberto unveiled a charcoal drawing that Alfonso immediately recognized were images of his grandparents, Carlo Chiappelli and Luisa Vivarelli.

"To each generation falls a hallmark in time," Alberto concluded. "The Etruscans were great believers in prophecies. They predicted that for the Chiappelli and others who boarded that ship with his cattle and grapes, it was the step of a thousand years. Chiappelli is the name of a family that originated in an Etruscan culture, survived one thousand years of Roman rule and provided a storied presence within an Italian region for another thousand years. We now are called to lead a thousand more."

chapter fourteen

T he next morning Alfonso departed with an oval-bordered charcoal portrait of himself held in a gold-painted frame and a charcoal drawing of his grandparents to carry along with his many other memories. The previous day he had been surprised to receive a request that he visit his Uncle Umberto. Alfonso had asked Riccardo to accompany him on this visit; Umberto was an uncle to both of them.

"I enjoyed the lectures," Alfonso said. "But I am not sure I completely understand the relevance."

"You are opening the age-old discussion of nature versus nurture," Riccardo responded. "The debate involves whether human behavior is determined by the environment, either prenatal or during a person's life, or by an individual's genetic inheritance and biological factors. The alliterative expression 'nature and nurture' has been in use since at least the Elizabethan period and goes back to medieval French.

"What you really are asking is why is genealogy important," Riccardo continued.

"Some further context will help understand this setting. Tracing all forebearers for 15 generations would provide a list of 32,768 names of ancestors. Although this certainly dilutes the influence of a specific lineage such as a focus on a paternal line, the greater import is the finding that the family has been located at that single location for more than 500 years. Most folks did not travel far from home, and the greatest factor influencing a selection for marriage is proximity.

"As the list of names in a genealogical search begins to step away from our own last name and incorporates all of the maternal and paternal bonds through time, a walk along the mountain trail will bring you to Casio Casola where the Sabatini family can still be found. The Lenzi family can still be found at Casa Poggio Barone, a small group of houses on the hilltop above Casio Casola. Vivarelli remains as a prominent name in Ponte della Venturina. Marconi is a name well regarded in Granaglione. Descendants of the Venturini and Poli families remain in Cireglio; the Giani and Santini families continue to be found at the Villa di Cireglio. The Pedruccioni family continues to live in Pavana, as does the Pierallini in San Felice.

"Interestingly, the name Borgognoni no longer is found in Granaglione; neither is the name of the hamlet, Capanne Molino, that had been synonymous with the Borgognoni family. The church that took the name Borgo Capanne remains." Riccardo had launched into his own lecture, presenting an impressive understanding of the regional history.

"Capanne means huts or very rough structures," he continued. "This location is a very old village. In the past the village was called Succida, a term from Latin succidere meaning to cut. The area was covered with a thick forest that was cut to make way for pasture. Residents built low, straw covered structures for their animals, hence Capanne. The word is still used in the area to signify a hay barn. By 1845 the area had become known as Ponte della Venturina. The bridge that was built over the Reno river established the new designation for the village previously known as Capanne Molino. Residents now numbered about 200. This time also finds the Borgognoni family no longer operating the mill.

"The mill ceased activity in 1905, the last miller was Beniamino Guccini. The structure was renovated and turned into a residence. It is worth remembering that in the registers of the Stato delle Anime (parish census) of the Parish church of Borgo Capanne, what now is known as Ponte della Venturina was for years called Molino or Molino da Reno.

"The village of Venturina began to grow mostly after 1845-50, the period in which the bridge was constructed for the opening of the road called the Porrettana. More growth was experienced after 1864 when the Bologna-Pistoia rail line was brought in and again after 1882 when the road to Pracchia was constructed, making the town an important crossroads. Ponte della Venturina became the population hub for the area and town center for Granaglione.

"As it continued to straddle the Tuscany-Emilia Romagna border, Ponte della Venturina served to separate the Tuscan Granduchy from the Papal States. In the early 1600s the Vatican customs office was located in a section called Castellina (on the right of the Reno), and not far away in an area near the bridge called Teglia the Granduchy established its custom house. When the new Porrettana road opened in the mid-1800s, traffic moved to the left bank of the Reno and two new customs houses were built."

The lecture concluded with their arrival in Granaglione. Alfonso and Riccardo walked purposefully to the Villa di Cireglio. Nobody followed.

Umberto apologized profusely for his bad manners and attempted to justify the beating he had administered to his wife. Diadema needed to learn her place, he said, suggesting that she had betrayed a trust.

"This war has changed everybody," Umberto began by way of explanation. "Everybody, regardless of social class or professional status, had to commit equally to support the war effort. We now expect to share equally in the rewards for our sacrifices.

"Almost every family had a relative on the war front," Riccardo offered by way of understanding. "The number of men and boys of enlisted to serve the military was about six million, at a time when Italy had only 7.5 million families; from that number, Italy suffered 460,000 soldiers killed and 955,000 wounded."

When the war began in 1914, Italy had 35 million citizens and was the sixth largest European nation. The recently formed nation remained mostly agricultural, underdeveloped, and illiterate, and was poor in comparison with the rest of Europe, with income half that of France. The post-unification message was: "now we have made Italy, we still have to make the Italians."

Italy was dependent on Britian for coal and steel, yet it was a member of the Triple Alliance with Germany and Austria-Hungary.

"Austria has been always been our enemy," Umberto maintained. "We had no business being tied up in that treaty.

"Irredentism," he shouted. "Redemption. Redemption of Italian territory."

Italy remained neutral when the war was declared, Riccardo explained. According to the terms of Triple Alliance agreement, if war involved more than two opposing countries Italy agreed to send its men to battle on the condition that Austria return to Italy territory that had been in dispute for centuries. The territory along the frontier of the two countries stretched from the Trentino region in the Alps eastward to Trieste at the northern end of the Adriatic Sea. Italian-speaking people populated much of that area.

The territory was not returned, Riccardo continued, so Italy negotiated the secret Pact of London that had been announced on 26 April 1915 whereby Italy entered the war in support of France and Great Britain with those nations supporting the Italian claim on the disputed territory.

"Irredentism," Umberto again shouted.

"How was the mobilization in your village," he asked Riccardo pointedly.

Italy had launched the Industrial Mobilization to support the war effort, an organization that controlled production and recruited manpower. The war engaged the entire population, including women and children. Women were assigned roles in metal working and mechanics. Boys aged 15 to 18 were assigned to the engineering corps and helped construct military structures at the front lines. The curriculum in elementary schools was changed radically, with children now immersed in the concepts of Motherland, war, and sacrifice.

"We lost the few workers we had left," Riccardo lamented. "We had barely enough food for ourselves, and the low prices fixed by the government only made things worse."

Alfonso assessed the scenario with stoic contemplation. Umberto certainly lacked the civility and refinement of the well-regarded Chiappelli family in Pistoia. Still, he was a close-blood relative and Umberto had an obvious passion for the people.

Everywhere it was easier for the rich to obtain food despite rationing, which fed resentment against the comparatively better off. The urban-rural antagonism that grew deep during the war created a divide that was becoming irreconcilable. As conditions worsened, age-old social divisions were sharpened and new divisions were created. Farmers were accused of hoarding supplies, leaving city-dwellers to starve. Discourse against profiteers often targeted Jews and turned into virulent antisemitism. Alfonso had learned that Diadema had befriended a peasant family; when Umberto had learned the family was Jewish, he beat his wife for continuing to help them.

Umberto continued to press the point that the hardships of war were equally distributed among the population. "This shared sacrifice is breaking down the social order," he said, "creating a climate where anger is being expressed openly in the streets."

"No compromise," Umberto insisted.

Riccardo interrupted to explain that until this Great War, the unification of Italy had been accomplished through political compromise. Giovanni Giolitti, the prime minister before the war, was a master of transformiso—the art of isolating the extreme right and extreme left wings in politics to build and maintain a centrist coalition.

"He was petit bourgeois," Umberto opined. "his ideas were small and lacked substance."

Alfonso and Riccardo accepted the conclusion of their host without challenge, as much from courtesy as from the exhaustive obsession over the issues. They seemed to agree on what needed to be accomplished, but differed on how to get the job done. At the train station they would head in separate directions, Riccardo traveling to Costigliole and Alfonso returning to the United States Army.

<hr />

THE QUESTION FOR ALFONSO REMAINED ELUSIVE, THOUGH seemingly he now had a multitude of answers.

Alfonso returned in time to entrain with the 117th on 2 April for staging at St. Nazaire, where the men boarded the *Walter S. Luckenbach* for the trip home, departing on 9 April. The 10-day voyage was rough, but uneventful, with the arrival in Brooklyn, New York, on Easter Sunday, 19 April 1919. After another train trip, Alfonso arrived for his last march in uniform at Camp Dix, New Jersey.

Alfonso spent much of his remaining time in discussion with Dr. McMains and others on what they would do after they arrived back home.

"You want to do more than just repair cars?" McMains challenged.

Alfonso took pride in being a 'wrencher.' "What more would you have me do?" he asked. They had had this conversation many times over.

"The most that you can do is the least that is expected of you," they repeated together.

Alfonso was part of a group of 'veterans' organized by Dr. McMains who had agreed to bond into an informal network through which they could share knowledge and secure financial backing, while maintaining the independence of their business activities. They had agreed to make a bulk purchase of surplus Army trucks, which would be individually owned.

"You do not make money buying trucks," McMains counseled. "You make money selling them, and cars, and then repairing them when they break down."

The group had made plans to share blueprints for constructing buildings and discussed standardizing inventories so that they could maximize their pool of money in making bulk purchases. They each had their agreed upon territory, but they knew that it would be a foolish to think that they would not be competing. Other veteran groups were coalescing, and those already back home had a head start.

Alfonso shared little about his visit to Italy. The trip was surreal. It seemed as if he was separated from his past by a glass window and the closer the ship drifted to America, the thicker that glass became.

OUTPROCESSING COULD NOT BE ACCOMPLISHED FAST ENOUGH, but hurry up and wait was now a seasoned response to military order. Alfonso approached the payroll desk, one of the last stops before receiving his final discharge documents. He had been queued in the line for most of the morning. The busy clerk did not look up and Alfonso remained anxious as he handed his papers forward.

"Chiappelli. What the hell kind of name is that," the clerk challenged.

"It is an American name," came the response from behind him, offered by Major James J. Tyson. The officer who certified the discharge papers for Alfonso on 25 April 1919 was the same officer who as a fresh lieutenant 1 ½ years previous had signed court martial charges against him. The major even recorded his last unit as the 117th Trench Motor Battery; replacing the mortar with the motor to acknowledge the contribution Alfonso had made.

Alfonso received $109.77, including $60 in bonus pay, and a pass to ride the railroad home to Cairnbrook, Pennsylvania.

EPILOGUE TO WAR SERVICE:

Clint Calvin Hearn died 11 February 1928. He retired as a Brigadier General in June 1919, then reentered the service in August 1919 and served as a Colonel in commanding coastal defenses from headquarters in Portland, Maine. Hearn was born 29 March 1866 in Weston, Texas. He was appointed to the military academy at West Point, New York, from which he graduated in 1890. He is buried at Arlington National Cemetery, Washington, DC, lot 2967.

⎯⎯⎯⎯⎯⎯⎯⎯⎯⎯⎯⎯⎯⎯

JOHN EDWARD MCGLOTHAN WAS FOUND DEAD IN HIS QUARTERS at the Marfa AAF Advanced Flying School, Texas, on 23 April 1943. Major McGlothan had been serving as Adjutant at the base.

McGlothan was born in Kentucky and grew up in Louisville. He continued to serve in the Army and was serving as an ROTC officer in Honolulu, Hawaii, when Pearl Harbor was attacked by the Japanese. A veteran of nearly 40 years of military service, Major McGlothan participated in the Mexican border dispute and both World Wars. He is buried in the Fort Sam Houston military cemetery, San Antonio.

chapter fifteen

The post-war years found Alfonso following plans precisely as planned. If the old adage applies that "man plans and god laughs," then this was a god with a wicked sense of humor. Cairnbrook had grown in the two short years since Alfonso had been gone, but that now was a lifetime ago and the growth was far short of what Alfonso now envisioned.

Back in 1914 when Alfonso had been learning auto repair at those classes taught in Pittsburgh, the students had been encouraged to subscribe to the Lincoln Highway Association. He became a lifetime member for $5. In later years it proved to be one of the soundest investments he ever made. In 1914 there were 1,664,003 licensed vehicles in the United States according to the association; by 1919 this number had quadrupled to 6,679,133.

Before the war there were almost no good roads to speak of in the United States. Roads around cities and large towns often were improved with a graded roadbed covered with gravel; the remainder of America's 2 ½ million miles of roads were little more than dirt paths, bumpy and dusty in dry weather and impassable in wet weather. The two-lane nine-mile road between Cairnbrook and Windber lay in this condition. Train was the preferred way to travel.

A coast-to-coast highway was the brainchild of Carl Fisher who had paved his Indianapolis Motor Speedway with bricks. Fisher promoted the construction of a graveled-covered highway spanning the continent; the cost, $10 million. The subscription drive ran into a roadblock set up by Henry Ford who maintained that the public would never learn to fund good roads if private industry did it for them. His point was well taken by Henry Joy, president of the Packard Motor Car Company, who suggested that efforts be redirected into a public education campaign to gain political support. He reasoned that since Congress had just approved $1.7 million for the construction of a marble memorial to Abraham Lincoln, the elected officials would be open to the even better tribute of a Lincoln Highway.

The new goal was to educate the country on the need for good roads made of concrete, with the Lincoln Highway to serve as an example of a this improvement. Some of the funds were used to provide 'seedling miles' in remote countryside locations to emphasize the superiority of concrete over unimproved dirt, with the idea that citizens would press their representatives to connect those patches of concrete road with continuous pathways throughout their state.

Alfonso had read about these plans in the newsletter and promotional flyers that came along with his lifetime subscription to the Lincoln Highway Association. He had traced the proposed map for this highway, following its trail from Times Square in New York City through New Jersey, Pennsylvania, Ohio, Indiana, Illinois, Iowa, Nebraska, Wyoming, Utah, Nevada, and California, ending in the Lincoln Park of San Francisco. He focused on the western Pennsylvania section and discovered that the proposed highway would pass within five miles of Cairnbrook. The association had organized a system of consultants along the highway who would act as local ambassadors; i.e., promoting the highway in local affairs, assisting visitors, and alerting headquarters of concerns with the road. Alfonso read with interest the report from Andrew Millot, an attorney from Somerset, who was advocating that access be provided for the Windber community by improving access to the Lincoln Highway with an improved connection through Cairnbrook. This was the driving force behind Alfonso's push for the Chiappelli family to remain at this location; older brother Dario and sister Armida had relocated to the eastern side of the state, near Philadelphia, and were urging the other family members to join them.

Alfonso had shared all of this information with Dr. McMains. This factored largely into their plans. The fall of 1919 found Alfonso sitting in the conference room of the First National Bank of Cairnbrook; with him at the table were the bank president, Michael V. Brant, and board of directors Jacob McGregor, Nelson C. Duberger, Washington Custer, and James M. Wagner. The board had just approved a loan to Alfonso Chiappelli, cosigned by Dr. Henry A. McMains, for an amount totaling $25,000, with an additional $10,000 credit line assigned to a draw account through which the veteran partnership would finance new car purchases and deposit sales receipts.

The loan was to be provided with an initial borrow of $15,000, with additional draws of $5,000 in each of the next two years. The business plan with action steps, detailed with supporting documents, measured out as a three-inch stack of paper that now was spread across the table. The initial loan of $15,000 would be used to purchase the blacksmith's barn, located at the top of McGregor Avenue on a plateau beginning the ridgeline overlooking the town, along with four quarter-acre plots of land that adjoined this property. The blacksmith building was constructed on a two-foot wide crushed stone foundation, with bay doors that opened to an expansive room created by the framework of massive chestnut beams. The space was large enough to park four cars, two at each side of a large work area. The loft provided a second story for living quarters; plans were in motion to renovate that area into two apartments with outside entrances.

Among the papers was a site plan that identified the location for a proposed car dealership. This building would be constructed facing northeast on the plot sited closest to the McGregor Avenue intersection with the Forbes Road, which trailed five miles to the Lincoln Highway. The site development plan identified the land to the east side of this proposed building designated as a staging site for car and truck sales. Two plots of land behind the proposed car dealership building were targeted for use as a truck depot. The blacksmith shop would be devoted to the maintenance of that fleet of vehicles after the car dealership opened.

Alfonso had formed three different business arrangements. He was a partner with Dr. McMains in the car dealership, a partner with Sam Adams in hauling freight with the trucks, and an independent proprietor of his repair garage incorporated as Cairnbrook Garage. He would own the buildings and land, sharing partnership in the inventory of cars and trucks. The timeline was aggressive. The business plan detailed the inventory of tools, equipment, parts and supplies that would be needed to support vehicles at the scale they envisioned.

He would begin selling cars immediately. Dr. McMains had provided the veterans cooperative with a bulk purchase opportunity of four dozen Buicks, with the delivery of four cars each month for the next 12 months. Alfonso had committed to selling one car a month. Funds would be drawn from the loan each month to buy a car to add to the inventory, with Alfonso sitting on that note until the car was sold; the longer the car stayed in the inventory, the higher the cost of the loan and the lower the return. Money moved when cars moved. Alfonso learned to sell, even though the grease beneath his fingernails betrayed his passion for doing repairs. Among his first acquisitions was a Packard truck that Alfonso outfitted for towing and field support.

He found his first customer in the bank president, Mr. Brant, who lived with his wife, no children, in a finely constructed house tucked neatly behind the powerful orange-brick presence of the bank building. The bank was located six buildings north of the site where Alfonso proposed to build his car dealership. The Forbes Road served as a dividing line between the company-owned coal town and private ownership; Alfonso had found a location seemingly straddling the bounds of both. On the east side of the road were facilities and activities all governed by mine management, beginning with the schoolhouse at the top of the hill and continuing down McGregor Avenue, with six streets lining up neat rows of the 200 housing units on the left and company-owned stores and movie house on the right. Other points of gathering, including a church and post office, were at the bottom of the hill near the mansion home of the mine superintendent.

Alfonso walked or drove past the bank building everyday enroute to the blacksmith shop which he had begun renting. with the option to buy, within a month of his return to Cairnbrook. The bank building was in alignment with the private commerce section of the blossoming town, with stores for groceries, meat, clothing, and hardware goods. An eight-room hotel with a dining room and bar had been constructed on the site to the east of the blacksmith building, now Cairnbrook Garage, and adjacent to the car dealership site. With miners willing to share sleeping quarters, the rooms sometimes held as many as two-dozen men.

Mr. Brant bought a 'money-green' 1920 Buick coupe for $700, marked up $200 above cost. Alfonso had advocated for the purchase of Buicks by the veterans group because of the 51 improvements made in design of the 1920 models.

"Changes included improved head lights, head light switch, head light dimmer and new Willard storage battery," Alfonso explained, "just to name a few." He quickly examined every 'fit and finish' on the vehicle, taking pleasure in the purr of the six-cylinder engine.

Before the year ended, the business model had been copied by others in the community; Wagner and Custer garages entered the competition, relatives of members of the bank board, but it was clear from the start that Alfonso had the 'economies of scale' advantage due to the combined purchasing power of the veterans buying together through their cooperative. Word was being whispered about that Alfonso Chiappelli was on the brink of a successful venture. One person in particular listened with great intent.

Although the Brants' did not have children of their own, they did have a live-in servant girl for whom they had developed great affinity. Jozefina Kvasnovsky was a string-bean sized just-turned teenager when she joined the household three years earlier. Jozefina now had blossomed into a long-legged beauty; she listened with keen interest when she served dinner to Mr. Brant, as the banker shed praise on Alfonso for his service to his country and commitment to helping grow Cairnbrook into a true American city. "The details of his plans were remarkable," Brant exclaimed, "he identified everything needed down to the paperclips."

Jozefina had endeared herself to the Brants, beginning with her fastidious attention to detail. She did not shirk a task. Indeed, unlike previous servant girls that Mrs. Brant had employed, Jozefina did not wait to be told what to do; if she did not have an assigned task she would find something extra to do, such as maintaining the vegetable garden and or trimming the shrubbery. It was behind some rhododendron and azalea bushes that Alfonso first saw Jozefina. "Her cat eyes captured me," he would later say. Jozefina had set herself up to be seen. She knew that Alfonso would be coming to the Brant house that day; she had been forewarned to keep herself hidden away, so she did—behind the bushes. Jozefina sized Alfonso up and devised her plan to 'bump' into him that evening—the movie man was in town and she was certain Alfonso would be in attendance.

Jozefina was the oldest of eight children; her family lived in the coal town of Hooversville, ten miles distant. Jozefina worked for the Brant family as a live-in servant during the week and ventured home on the weekends; it was a trip she did not enjoy. From her perspective, the only interest her parents had in having her come home was to demand that she hand over her wages and clean up the house, beginning with picking up and dusting out the coal-laden clothes that were always piled at the entrance, and minding after her brothers and sisters whilst her parents got drunk on homemade whiskey with the boarders who rented bed space in a cramped downstairs room. The family sleeping quarters were in a second-story loft, with a canvas tent stretched over an oak frame serving as an extension to the house and providing a dining area for all inhabitants. The refinement of the Brant home and the shabbiness she found with her parents lifestyle imprinted a resentment that would forever stamp her days.

In the Brant household, Jozefina was learning to appreciate the comforts that came from monetary success. The Brants were deeply patriotic, emphasizing that America was the land of opportunity—

they were quick to note that their ancestors had been indentured servants—and cited themselves as examples of success. Jozefina took special note of every command directed by Mrs. Brant who was quite outspoken in stating the difference between right and wrong. Jozefina was determined to do all things American. She had benefited from an elementary level education where she mastered the basic reading, writing, and arithmetic. One of the benefits of working for Mrs. Brant was access to reading material; the bank had subscriptions to several newspapers, including this note in the *Somerset Herald*:

> "The 'movie' man has discovered that Central City is on the map and his place of entertainment is crowded every night. Among the most interested patrons of the film show are John Wechtenhiser and his wife, former owners of the site on which the playhouse is erected, who remarked that in their 70 years they never had attended a professional entertainment…"

The report continued with notice that the movie man would be sharing his entertainment in Cairnbrook the next week. Jozefina had cleaned her best garments, which included modified hand-me-downs from Mrs. Brant, opted for sandal-type shoes to reduce her height and patted down and pinned her hair. She stood five feet, nine inches tall—the difference in her height concerned her more than the 10 years difference in age; Jozefina towered over Alfonso by four inches.

At first annoyed, Mrs. Brant had moved quickly in support of the quest when her husband had remarked that Jozefina looked like a mature women, "and acts like one, thanks to you." Mrs. Brant responded with that new cliché liberals were using to accommodate the immigrants: "we are in the melting pot."

Jozefina moved with feline grace in her bump into Alfonso on that and every opportunity that followed. Alfonso returned the 'bump' with a bit more masculine intent, resulting in an unexpected present for Jozefina to remember her 16th birthday on the 4th of March in 1921—she was pregnant.

It was typical of Italian men to marry women much younger then themselves. It was given as a natural arrangement that mothers would nurture their sons for as long as they were able, and mothers often influenced the selection of the young bride who would replace her in caregiving. Alfonso had moved back into the comfort of his mother's nurturing upon his return from the war. Giuseppina had been floating the names of young women who might be considered to take her place; she was in declining health, as she had never completely recovered from the miscarriage experienced in the month before the family move from Starford. Alfonso noted that the anglicized name for Giuseppina and also for Jozefina was Josephine; with his mother's blessing, actually her insistence upon learning of the pregnancy, Alfonso transferred his loyalty from one Josephine to another.

This was not accomplished without friction. The immediate obstacle was the Catholic priest, an Irishman who relished in his despise of Italians who ventured from the guidance of the church. He had singled out Egisto as a sinner who deserved his time in prison. Alfonso had never stepped a foot into the local Catholic church and he was not going to start now.

The Kvasnovsky family proved to be the polar opposite, with a devotion to the Catholic church that went beyond question or measure. Stefan Kvasnovsky, Jozefina's father, had been five years old when he was made an orphan ward of the Catholic Church. Stefan was born in Oscadnica, Slovakia; he was the youngest son among five children born to Josef Kvasnovsky and wife Sofia Moszor. Josef died tragically in a fire that left a grieving widow unable to care for her children. The priest assigned to the local church in Oscadnica, Saint Stephen Catholic Church, was a distant relative and agreed to take Stefan into his care. Beyond all of their faults, Jozefina had always found solace in the Kvasnovsky commitment to the church;

160

the local priest was known to share a sip or two when visiting their home. Embracement of Catholic values was the redeeming act of her family that would continue to secure her loyalty. Jozefina herself was born in Oscadnica, having been carried to America in her mother's arms when she was a baby of two years. She insisted upon the blessing of a priest and a marriage ceremony in a Catholic Church.

The impasse was broken by a surprise suggestion from Egisto. "Buy an indulgence," he muttered. A contribution of $200 in the name of the Stefan Kvasnovsky family was made to a fund to rename the Catholic Church in Oscadnica, Slovakia. The church had been called Saint Stephen's from its origin to acknowledge a Hungarian king; in 1921 the people of Oscadnica felt that no longer was necessary and henceforth the Church of Assumption served the community. On a wall inside the entrance door is a framed image of Josephine Kosnosky, the now anglicized name that she printed on the photograph that was sent to the church along with the largest donation ever received.

Alfonso Chiappelli and Josephine Kosnosky were married in a civil ceremony at the courthouse in Bedford, Pennsylvania, on 17 October 1921. Rena Maria Chiappelli was born on 5 December 1921 to the delight of her grandmother Giuseppina who, with Etruscan prophecy, stated: "This is the child who will take my place."

Giuseppina Chiappelli died on 11 April 1922 from a cerebral hemorrhage; she was 50 years in age.

chapter sixteen

The Federal Highway Act of 1921 provided $75 million in matching funds to states for highway construction, with the requirement that states identify seven percent of total road mileage as 'primary'; monies would be matched only for the construction of these roads. For the states that were linked by the Lincoln Highway, the choice was obvious; the path through Pennsylvania was so designated and the dollars were matched with progress that smoothed the way down the mountainside of the Allegheny Plateau in Somerset County to the valley of neighboring Bedford.

The significance of this link was not lost on Alfonso, although it took him a while to explain it to Sam Adams. It had slowly dawned on Alfonso, after the trucking partnership had been launched with Sam and the real work began, that he had transferred much of his expectations based on conversations that he had had with Paul Canfield moments before a German bomb altered that dream. Sam was a good man, a solid worker. His skill at chauffeuring a truck had already earned him the title 'king of the road.' Sam understood less, however, the intricacies of logistical support that kept those trucks running. Alfonso was determined to teach him.

They had acquired two dozen trucks through Army surplus sells, half of which were good only for spare parts. Dr. McMains was monitoring the inventory being made available. "You will want Packards, of course," he had quizzed Alfonso before the purchases were made, and was a bit surprised at the emphasis Alfonso put into his answer "no."

"Macks. Diamond-Ts. Whites, if you can find them."

"Macks have the radiators behind the engine," McMains answered. "That might have been useful in the battlefield, but you will have overheating problems on those mountain roads. Why do you want them?" The doctor had heard the details of Alfonso's exploits at Grandpre when they were back in Germany. "You might not get fancy medals or promotions like others," Dr. McMains had shared in consolation. "Those are for guys who are career military; they need that glory. Word gets around. The men know who gets the job done."

"...the least expected of me," Alfonso had responded with a sly grin.

"Heavier payloads," Alfonso explained. "Get the trucks with the largest chassis. Every vehicle will be reconstructed to fit into our specifications. That will help standardize the parts inventory."

He now was trying to determine what was the least he could expect from Sam. Alfonso explained that the resources in the Shade Creek area had been unleashed with the purchase of 1,100 acres by Theodore Garish from the Walker family. Mr. Garish began a mass harvest of the virgin timber, with designs to dig out the coal that lay beneath. In order to market his products he and financial backers in Pittsburgh proposed to construct a railroad over the mountains to connect the urban needs of Pittsburgh with the produce-rich Bedford Valley; the Walker location was sited at the middle of this planned construction. The central location was to serve as the main railroad yard, with logistical support shops; that is why it was called Central City.

Subsequent decisions from the Pittsburgh financiers drastically altered those plans. The coal was directed to the steel plants in Johnstown and areas beyond via a railroad connection through Windber. The central railroad yard never made it beyond paper.

Alfonso could see that Sam's attention was drifting away from the conversation. "What this means," he said to connect the dots for Sam, "is that we can finish the connection to the Bedford market. Coal and timber products still need to be hauled to those areas. The drive will be all downhill from Cairnbrook with the heavy loads.

And hopefully filled with lighter loads of agricultural goods that we truck back up the mountain on the return trip. Those are the freight contracts that you want to go after," Alfonso said to completely spell out the opportunity for Sam.

Alfonso was in the transportation business, moving whatever he could in his trucks and cars; this included people. He had taught Josephine to drive and she was a quick study in whatever vehicle she encountered. She had helped him rebuild several engines; she knew which tools to hand to him and when he needed them. Josephine even was able to understand a schematic drawing and comprehend the assembly of parts. By act of the god of fate, Alfonso had found the partner he needed. Alfonso accepted a contract to transport children to school from the outlying areas; he hired Josephine to be the bus driver, a career she continued for 56 years. Beginning in 1922, drivers were required to be licensed to operate a vehicle on a public road; Josephine was among the first to gain her license and was one of the few women to do so.

Alfonso and Josephine had moved into one of the blacksmith apartments. His worry was with his father. Egisto now was a widower with two teenage children in his care. As it had always been, the Chiappelli homestead was a magnet for casual gathering in the community. Now that prohibition was being enforced, those who gathered sometimes came from locations more distant and left with quantities large enough to draw attention.

The community needed a place for social gathering, Alfonso concluded. The location needed to be a neutral site where mine workers and management could meet as equals; a place where immigrants from different countries could mix; a place owned by the people; and most importantly, a place that would keep the crowd away from his father's house. It was through this inspiration that the Cairnbrook Community Club was born, with Alfonso a founding member and the rational voice that convinced a skeptical mine management to help with the financing. Certainly his status as a WWI veteran was a factor, but mine management noted that his uncle, Pio Chiappelli, was a survivor of an explosion at the Starford Coal Mine in which 36 miners were killed. The disaster happened on Saturday, 26 Jan 1924, and the mine superintendent was among the victims.

The story of Pio Chiappelli is included as a supplemental chapter at the end of this tale in a novelette titled, "The Door Down."

A yellow-brick building was designed as a two-story structure, with the first level constructed at a sub-level (basement); the building site was a half-mile south of the Cairnbrook Garage along the Forbes Road. The Club was dedicated to the community at an opening on the 4th of July 1924. A beauty contest held as part of this celebration was won by Mary Louise Chiappelli, youngest sister of Alfonso. It was at this event that Louise caught the eye of a young Italian immigrant, Arturo Vespa, with whom she was married in October of that year.

The plan was coming together. As Alfonso had anticipated, there was need to replace the brake pads on the trucks with inordinate frequency; trying to hold back the weight as the trucks descended those steep mountain grades into the Bedford valley was burning the brakes and grinding out transmissions. He had prepared for routine replacement of both. He had not planned on replacing as many trucks that they were losing to accidents, nor was he happy that the trucks sat out of service awaiting maintenance repairs that could be accomplished by the drivers. Certainly they could learn how to do more than change a flat tire; they had to learn how to keep those beasts on the road. On most days, except Sunday, they were able to keep four trucks in continuous transport.

Alfonso was selling cars, Sam was hauling freight with a team of drivers, and Josephine was driving bus. The repair shop was kept open extended hours with the part time help from a novice apprentice, his younger brother Hugo who would soon reach age 16.

Alfonso acknowledged to himself that the binding ingredient that was making all of his business plans come together was his wife Josephine. She was a ball of energy. Josephine set the agenda for a daily routine, except Sunday, when she would attend mass at the Catholic Church and he would stay home and say not a word.

She would prepare breakfast while he attended to his morning ablutions; she would attend to her needs while he ate. Rena had the run of the room, but mostly she just sat in her father's lap as she was wont to do whenever possible. Alfonso had bonded with his daughter from the day she was born; rocking her to sleep had been his job. "Every father should want a daughter," Alfonso had bragged to his friends, "so he will have someone to care for him in his old age." As he hugged his Rena to his chest he chuckled at his thought that he truly had found a replacement for his mother—Giuseppina had nurtured him as a baby, and his Rena would nurture him when he became an old baby—it was the Tuscan custom.

Josephine would clean up the dishes, and Rena, while Alfonso descended the steps into the garage. The steps reached a landing at the north side of the building which provided the option of opening a door that enabled egress to and from the apartment, or opening a door that accessed a stairway that continued into the garage. On the north side of the apartment was a window through which Josephine could see the Brant house; Mrs. Brant had become part of their routine, demanding daily visits with Rena and insisting that she provide be allowed to provide childcare while Josephine assisted in the garage. In the absence of a mother-in-law or other maternal influence, she had taken an active role in helping Josephine organize her household.

It was through this surrogate arrangement with Mrs. Brant that American values continued to be imprinted on Josephine. These were not always compatible with the care-free lifestyle of her parents. Stefan Kvasnovsky had ventured from the Tatra Mountains of Slovakia at the direction of the Catholic priest who had arranged for his employment as a miner in America. He had immigrated to America in September 1904 soon after his marriage to Maria Potochar and was not present for the birth of Josephine in March of the following year.

Mrs. Brant could not have known that the world's first melting pot that mixed a European variety of ethnicity had occurred 700 years ago in those same Tatra Mountains. The original tribes of Celts, Saxons and Slavs who by the 1200s had mixed their cultures in the isolation of the mountains were joined in the next three centuries by Germans, Slovaks, Poles, Wallachians, Romanians, Russians, Baltic shepherds, and Hungarian nobles—all with one factor in common, they were survivors who had escaped the onslaught of successive invading armies, ranging from the unforgiving Huns to the viscous Tartars.

By the 1800s, the town of Oscadnica had coalesced within that remote and rugged region in the form of 306 houses and 2,987 inhabitants who survived the harsh climate and infertile soil by developing an economy of sheep breeding, stock breeding, milk, wool, and leather processing. They were a people called 'Gorals' whose fierce independence and love for "szlebodu" (freedom) caused many to call them gypsies. They were distinct in their dialect, farming practices, architecture, dress, music, cuisine, and mindset. The Gorals had no identity with a national governance, all were foreign; they mostly had been left alone by the various empires who had claimed to rule the region. They were, however, endeared to the Catholic Church. The family name in the Goral dialect was Qvasznovszkj.

The daily routine fell into a schedule that included Rena returning from her daycare with Mrs. Brant in time for an afternoon siesta nap with Alfonso, during which time Josephine laid out a meal. Josephine then would return to the garage where she would wipe clean the tools, returning to the designated location each tool not needed, and organizing all tools and parts needed for the next repair job. She was relentless in knocking the mud and dirt away from the engine that Alfonso would repair, maintaining that a quality job began with a clean engine.

Alfonso would return to work, Rena in tow. The job at hand and Rena's behavior would determine how long Josephine stayed to assist before drifting back to her domestic tasks upstairs, later joined by Alfonso, on most days far late into the night with a warmed-over dinner.

Alfonso was recalling the autumn day of 1924 when his daily routine was disregarded in order to watch a team of men begin the tasks of digging out a foundation and staging materials for the construction of a modern state-of-the-art car dealership. The blueprints were spread across a stack of the stone-cut faced concrete block that Alfonso had insisted upon for the primary building material. He wanted materials that reflected a permanent standing in the community. He had pointed out on the blueprints to Josephine, Mrs. Brant and her husband, and to anyone who cared to know, the plan for an impressive showroom, customer service area, air compressor and hydraulic lift, office, and storage room for parts and supplies. He would locate gasoline pumps at the front; two tanks—1,000-gallon for regular gas, and 500-gallon capacity for a premium grade—were being buried in the ground.

Pumps to those tanks now were being installed. Alfonso was giving an update to a group of men who had gathered at the Club; naturally they were curious to get a full report on the construction details. "Thank goodness we got underroof before the snows arrived," Alfonso repeated. "We will not have to deal with the god damn mud." The work now had moved indoors, with the entire building being wired for electricity. The car dealership would be ready to open with the arrival of Spring.

"Why did you not build three years ago when you were renovating the blacksmith shop?" someone asked.

"Cash flow," Alfonso responded. "and training. We needed to work our way to this moment."

"You sure have hit the jackpot now. A beautiful wife, a precious daughter, and a baby due in mid-Spring. Do you have names picked out?"

"All of our children's names will begin with 'R,'" Alfonso said. "We agreed on a letter to narrow the choice to a mutual decision. If it is a girl, she will be named Rosina, if a boy, Raymundo."

"What are you doing here today, on a Friday afternoon? Is this one of those Italian holidays?" someone teased.

Alfonso laughed. "My daughter's birthday. Ended work early to celebrate after she gets up from her afternoon nap."

"She is a little girl, not a baby," he said, in mimic of her repeated statement throughout the morning.

"I guess you know what my next question is going to be?"

"No. But I will give you an answer anyway," Alfonso said wittingly.

The banter was disrupted by a noise unlike any Alfonso had ever heard before; it was the sound of a wounded animal. This animal was human.

Moments later a breathless youngster rushed into the Club and choked out the message. With each intake of air exchanged for an outtake of word, he breathed the news—your—garage—on—fire.

Alfonso rushed to the scene to find men shoveling snow onto a blaze that had fully engulfed the Cairnbrook Garage. "Rena…"

Her name was still echoing in his first awareness weeks later as he began to recover from his catatonic state. Events were explained to him in slowly consumed pieces as he struggled to recover an awareness of his presence in life.

Rena died in a fire. Alfonso was brought back to the home of his father where he now was sitting on the porch. His wife was still recovering from third-degree burns. She was badly injured.

He had a wife? Alfonso had misplaced that memory. Newspaper reports summarized the results of the fire; neighbors filled in details.

Josephine was in a rush to complete preparations for the birthday celebration. Earlier that day Rena had stood still long enough for a photograph to be made—a present from Mrs. Brant who had taken her to the sitting. A later brush against a grease can had soiled the clothes Rena wore for the photo, her very best. Josephine had just finished sprucing her up for the party and Rena wanted to show Mrs. Brant the clean they had restored to her dress.

Through the window, Josephine could see Mrs. Brant walking down the side road that provided a path through the neighborhood. She helped Rena don her coat and watched as Rena started to walk down the stairs, with the careful, clumsy one-step-at-a-time progress of a happy three-year-old. Josephine had approved and turned her attention to cleaning up the stove from which she had recently removed a cake, part of an American tradition to celebrate the observance of aging.

In her rush to clean, Josephine grabbed a rag that she had used to clean the grease from Rena's dress. The rag had been soaked in kerosene. The explosion of flames engulfed the dress shirt that Josephine had tucked neatly into her long skirt, an ensemble usually reserved for Sunday church attendance. In confusion and pain she slapped at the fire burning her throat and chest and fumbled her way to the exit door as flames chased her down the steps. Falling to the ground, she was rolled over by Mrs. Brant who screamed "where is Rena."

CAIRNBROOK TOT BURNED TO DEATH

Rena Chiapella Perishes in Flames; Two Buildings Destroyed; $15,000 Loss

CAIRNBROOK, Dec. 6.—In a blaze that destroyed a two-story frame garage and dwelling building owned by Alphonse Chiapella here late yesterday afternoon, little Rena Chiapella, aged three years, only child of Mr. and Mrs. Chiapella, was burned to death. The flames quickly spread and the home of Harry Thomas, adjoining the Chiapella building, also was destroyed. The total loss on the Chiapella building is estimated at about $12,000, while Mr. Thomas' loss was about $3,000.

The fire broke out about 2:30 o'clock when a combustible fluid used by Mrs. Chiapella in cleaning clothing exploded. Before Mrs. Chiapella could rescue her little daughter the second floor was a mass of flames and her loved one was trapped in the burning building. The charred bones of the little Chiapella girl have not yet been recovered from the ruins.

The Chiapella building was used as a garage on the first floor, while the second floor was made into apartments, occupied by the Chiapella family, Mrs. C. Paul and the William Dixon family. All of the household goods in the building were consumed. Four automobiles stored in the garage also were destroyed.

As a result of the explosion Mrs. Chiapella suffered painful burns about the face and hands. She was removed to the home of a neighbor, where she is resting fairly well today.

Members of the Cairnbrook Volunteer Fire Company responded to an alarm and the Central City volunteer laddies also were summoned. The firemen bravely fought the flames but were handicapped in their work because of an inadequate water supply.

FOUNDRY BURNS.

"With you," Josephine shouted, "Rena is with you," she yelled again as she scrambled to her feet, realizing that her statement now held false hope. Josephine rushed toward the building directly into a blow-back of flame that, combined with a full-body tackle by Mrs. Brant, threw her into a bank of snow. Skin began to peal from her wounds in her struggle. Other neighbors had arrived by then. Josephine was subdued and moved into the spare bedroom of the Brant home where she had stayed a few years previous.

One observer reported "the coal mine siren went off, and when we answered the call the manager told us to go help put out a fire. We knew the fire was up on the hill because we could hear the screaming echoing down into the valley. It took four strong men to hold that woman from rushing back into the fire."

The news was shouted in headlines throughout the region. The most complete account was provided in the evening edition of *The Johnstown Tribune* newspaper on Saturday, 6 December 1924.

Josephine replayed the sequence of events over and over again until she convinced herself that Alfonso ultimately was to blame. She had heard Rena open a door, but it must have been the door leading to the garage; Rena was searching for Alfonso because he had been gone for an extended period of time. If Alfonso had been home to help with the preparations, she would not have been so rushed, Josephine reasoned to herself.

Her anguish then evolved to conclude that the fire was a providence of faith; if she had been married in the Catholic Church as she had demanded, the fire would not have happened. A fire had taken the life of her grandfather and orphaned her father to the Church. This was a fire of retribution, and the fault lay completely with Alfonso. Josephine kept these thoughts to herself, but was obsessed with the fact that Alfonso was absent on Sunday the 7th of December when the Catholic priest so generously consecrated the still smoldering remains of the Cairnbrook Garage, sprinkling the grounds with holy water as he encircled the burned-out building. Josephine had been assisted out of her bed and placed in a chair at the front of a makeshift altar that the priest used to say mass and repeat the words ingrained in the funeral rites…ashes to ashes, dust to dust. The ashes of Rena Chiappelli found their lasting rest within the foundation walls of the building; no remains were recovered. In the Depression years the land was sold and a house was built on that foundation.

Josephine demanded to see Alfonso; on Christmas Day she received her wish. Josephine was prepared for a confrontation. She expected that Alfonso might appear contrite. She had done all she could to save Rena; where was he? She was prepared to challenge Alfonso regardless of his excuse; she was not prepared for his state of withdrawal.

From that moment forward, Josephine took command. Alfonso was returned to his father's home to convalesce. Mrs. Brant insisted that Josephine would remain with her until after Josephine gave birth. She would figure out how to return the Brant generosity at a later date; for now Josephine had to tend to her own recovery, painful as it would prove to be. Her skin, which had been stretched with pregnancy, was extensively burned down the front of her body. Scars would forever more peek out of her garments at the neck and show if she wore a shirt with short sleeves. For her remaining days, which were many, Josephine wore expansive sunbonnets or sat under an umbrella on sunny days because any exposure to the sun would produce excruciating pain.

With the help and guidance of Mrs. Brant, Josephine arranged for the rental of a house four buildings to the south of the car dealership. A wet nurse was located, Josephine would not be able to breastfeed, and a local spinster was hired as a live-in helper. Mrs. Brant bought furnishings for the new home, which featured a magnificent railing on the staircase leading to the second floor.

Sam Adams was able to keep the same number of trucks on the road, thanks in large measure to the extensive effort Alfonso had made to keep a reserve fleet in repair. Josephine turned her concern to the more immediate needs identified in the repair log which now occupied multiple sheets in the ledger. The backlog of work soon would impact their ability to deliver freight. Help came from an unexpected source.

Hugo stood up to the task. He brought the repair logs to Josephine who helped him prioritize the needed work, identifying the trucks from which he could scavenge parts. Enough tools were found in the supplies that had arrived for the car dealership to enable work to continue. Insurance coverage had been arranged through the Wagner Insurance Agency and the settlement, when it eventually arrived, would cover the financial loss. Dr. McMains had sent word that replacement cars were on the way.

Hugo provided oversight on the construction activity. The architectural design for the car dealership called for the construction of an 8-foot by 30-foot rectangle providing a second-story façade at the front of the building. Hugo directed that the business name be painted in that rectangular frame proclaiming in large letters, Cairnbrook Garage. He said he wanted to tell the community that they were still in business.

After the initial response of sympathy and curiosity, there was no further outpouring of support from the community. Tragedies were common, with children often losing their lives in mine accidents or farm mishaps; rampant disease, such as the flu epidemic of 1918, also took their toll.

chapter seventeen

With the beginning of the new year, Alfonso began daily visits, and Josephine began a daily routine of giving him definitive directions on what to do. By the end of the month, Alfonso was leaving the daily visits in the company of Hugo; together they went to work at rebuilding the Cairnbrook Garage. Alfonso began to thrive with the concentrated focus on the business of making money –structuring the work flow, restocking the inventory, expanding the repair service with equipment to machine and rebuild engines, increasing the capacity of the trucking fleet.

Those daily visits had been prescribed by Dr. Knight Dunlap. In the week prior to Christmas, Dr. McMains had arrived from Baltimore bringing in tow Dr. Dunlap, a research psychologist at The Johns Hopkins University who was establishing a reputation for himself as he advanced his theory of 'reaction psychology.' Dr. McMains had befriended Dunlap during the war when both took an interest in the theory of "shell shock" and advocated for further study and care of veterans returning from the world war. "The term 'shell shock' was coined by the soldiers themselves," Dr. McMains explained to Josephine. "Symptoms included fatigue, tremor, confusion, nightmares and impaired sight and hearing. It was often diagnosed when a soldier was unable to function and no obvious cause could be identified."

During the war, McMains had supported the efforts of medical personnel to cure shell shock through cognitive and affective reintegration. He agreed with the psychologists who concluded that shell-shocked soldiers were attempting to manage their traumatic experience by repressing or splitting off any memory of the event. Symptoms, such as tremor or contracture, were the product of an unconscious process designed to maintain the dissociation, he explained, thus a patient could be cured only if his memory were revived and integrated within his consciousness.

When the field of psychology was introduced as a branch of medical practice in the mid-1800s, it was defined as the science of consciousness; the primary technique for diagnosis was introspection—looking within. This method of psychoanalysis which involves the patient talking about their experiences and selves was popularized by Sigmund Freud whose ideas were influential in the study of lifespan development, personality, and therapy. Although many therapists believed strongly in the unconscious and the impact of early childhood experiences on the rest of a person's life, this introspection failed to gain support from the scientific community because of a major problem; without measurement, there was no way to resolve differences of opinion. This proved to be a fatal flaw when people reported different introspections under similar conditions.

Carl Gustav Jung, an associate of Freud, recognized this flaw and insisted on an empirical psychology on which theories must be based on facts and not on the psychologist's projections or expectations. He defined four mental functions which relate

- Sensation, which tell consciousness that something is there.

- Feelings, which consist of value judgments, and motivate our reaction to what we have sensed.

- Intellect, an analytic function that compares the sensed event to all known others and gives it a class and category, allowing us to understand a situation within a historical process, personal or public.

- Intuition, a mental function with access to deep behavioral patterns, being able to suggest unexpected solutions or predict unforeseen consequences, "as if seeing around corners" as Jung put it.

In 1913, John B. Watson declared he was a new type of psychologist—a behaviorist. Watson said the behaviorist would completely eliminate introspection from psychology, studying only things that could be observed and measured. He said this would allow scientists to control human behavior and explained this claim about the potential power of behaviorism in a best-selling book titled *Psychology as the Behaviorist Views It*. The central tenet of early behaviorism was that psychology should be a science of behavior, not of the mind, and rejected internal mental states such as beliefs, desires, or goals. By the 1920s psychologists were more likely to define their field as the science of behavior. Behaviorists argued that truly scientific psychologists should study only observable behavior.

Knight Dunlap, who had been a colleague with Watson at The Johns Hopkins University, was articulating a reaction psychology that blended attacks on introspection, instinct, and images, with what he said was "an insistence on response or reaction as the basis of mental processes, including thought processes and consciousness." Dunlap had joined the staff at Johns Hopkins in 1906 and held the title of Professor of Experimental Psychology. His time at Hopkins was interrupted with service with the Medical Research Laboratory of the Air Service during the world war. He proposed a theory that combined the analysis of the mental state with an assessment of behaviors. In order to advance his theory into practice, Dunlap needed data; his study of Alfonso Chiappelli and Jozefina Kvasnovsky provided a treasure-trove of material that informed later classification of behavioral development into the widely used Dunlap scale.

Dunlap detailed his findings in his consultation with Dr. McMains. In detail, he explained how individuals develop their ability to function in society through an evolution of their environment, and in response to their physiological abilities. Early in life, individuals are imprinted with values of good and bad from the environment created by their parents. As their sphere expands with influence from teachers and religious leaders, individuals begin to choose their "heroes;" that is, they model the people they would like to be when they grow up. By the time they reach their age of maturity, most individuals will have attached themselves to a peer group from whom they gain their social acceptance.

Behavioral patterns are locked in by the time an individual reaches adulthood, Dunlap lectured, unless that pattern of development is interrupted by a significant life event. Alfonso has had an insult at each stage of his behavioral development; Dr. Dunlap listed the major significant emotional events:

- age 6, absence of father for two years.
- age 8, emigrated to America never again to see his grandparents.
- age 16, separated from his father and older brother who were sent to prison.
- age 17, involved in altercation that resulted in his discharging a pistol and shooting his younger brother.
- age 22, drafted into military service.
- age 25, pressured into marriage.
- age 27, death of his mother.
- age 30, death of his daughter.

"Any one of those events would alter the development of an individual," Dr. Dunlap concluded.

"What do you recommend?" McMains asked. He noted that during the war, psychologists identified three essentials for treatment of shock—promptness of action, suitable environment and psychotherapeutic measures.

"Treatment measures often were limited to encouragement and reassurance," McMains said. "Alfonso will get plenty of that, but we need to prescribe something more specific."

"I concur," said Dunlap, "and I do have a suggestion. He must focus on becoming an American."

"He is an American," McMains protested. "What do you mean?"

"Look at the pattern of his development," Dunlap argued. "Every significant insult can be traced to his family, particularly to his father. His admirable characteristics emerged when he served as an American soldier. He must split from his family influence."

It cannot be determined how much the recommendation of Dr. Dunlap was influenced by Mrs. Brant and his interviews with Josephine. Nonetheless, the scene was set, driven by a determination from Josephine that began with decisiveness and eventually became overbearing. Alfonso would spend the remaining 50 years of his life in the shadow of the dominating presence of Josephine. She was driven in her control.

With the renewal of Spring, Alfonso had regained his public self; he was comfortable interacting with his business partners and customers in the same professional manner that previously had earned their loyalty. The arrival of his old friend Dr. McMains had prompted Alfonso to break down a bit of his introverted shell. The arrival of his son had produced the opposite reaction.

When Josephine attempted to hand over to Alfonso their newborn bundled in a cotton wrap, a son she named Raymond Joseph who had been born prematurely on 20 March 1925, Alfonso reacted with dismay at the contact. Never once did Alfonso ever hold his son, or any child for that matter. He was an excellent provider, a strong father figure as a teacher and mentor. Affection was not part of the equation.

With each of the progressive steps through which Alfonso seemingly rejected family, Josephine stepped in with more dominant control. The pattern was chiseled in stone—marble to be specific.

Rumors had been abundant that Egisto was carrying on an inappropriate relationship with the wife of a local miner who was dying from a lung disease. Within a month of the death of that miner in 1926, Pia Conti moved into the household of Egisto, along with her 12-year-old son. Egisto and Pia forged a union of 30 years, equal in length to the years of marriage Egisto had with Giuseppina, but it was never recognized by the church, nor by civil authorities.

Alfonso responded with indifference. His younger sister, Mary Louise, had been married in 1924 and although Hugo continued to live with his father, Egisto was an empty-nester and alone. He was entitled to his comforts.

Josephine was a bit more demonstrative in her reaction to the living arrangement. She complained that their public image was smudged and that their business would suffer as a result. This was a sin, Josephine whined; the Catholic priest would cite this as another example of heathen behavior.

Josephine insisted that they change their last name to "Chappell."

The proposal was met with a silence frozen as an age in an iceberg. Alfonso had never discussed with Josephine his visit back to Italy with his post-war furlough. Until this moment, he had not embraced the significance of that visit, nor his last name.

The terms of their relationship were established for their remaining years together. With a response that clearly was not open for debate, Alfonso carefully stated that his last name was, is, and would forever be, Chiappelli, and that he would acknowledge his marriage to her and their children by that name and no other. Beyond that single simple requirement, Alfonso would concede to Josephine all other decisions regarding family.

Josephine accepted those terms. She began by driving a permanent wedge with her father-in-law by arranging for the placement of a marble tombstone at the gravesite of Giuseppina Chiappelli. The funereal tradition of Tuscany would have called upon Egisto to reclaim the bones from the burial site and place them in the family sarcophagus. As a compromise to that tradition, Egisto had decided to leave an unmarked wooden cross with the buried remains of

Giuseppina. Josephine justified her actions by telling Alfonso that a tombstone was an American requirement.

The birth of two more sons—Richard Philip on 3 May 1927 and Raphael Mark on 21 Jan 1929—did little to soften their distance as Josephine took complete command of family matters while Alfonso spent an increased amount of his leisure time at the Cairnbrook Community Club. When the hen-pecking reached the tolerance limit for Alfonso, he would respond with "oh, boo-ba-boo," a cue that never seemed to stop Josephine from continuing with her verbal demands, but always signaled that Alfonso had stopped listening.

As a matter of routine, Alfonso carried in his front pants pockets daily receipts from the garage; a 'change bag' containing coins from the cash register was in the right pocket, with paper money folded and held in a gold clip tucked into the left. He would walk the short distance home after closing the garage at the end of the day, carrying the proceeds to the kitchen table where he would separate the intake of cash from the amount placed in the register each morning to facilitate transactions. On occasion he would walk past his home and continue on to the Club. The birthdate of his youngest son in January 1929 marked one of those days, memorable for Alfonso more due to the aftermath then the birth itself.

Alfonso paid for a round of drinks at the Club in celebration, shared cigars, and sat for a couple of rounds of cards at the poker table. He enjoyed a few shots of whiskey in response to toasts offered by others who had joined in the celebration, including downing the contents of a glass handed to him by a distant acquaintance, a competitor in the auto repair business to whom he occasionally sold spare parts. Alfonso remembered that drink the following morning when he was found sprawled across the porch at the front door to his home, with the pockets of his pants turned inside out.

The details for events that resulted are few. The *Meyersdale Republic* newspaper on 29 Jan 1929 published the fact that Alfonso had been indicted by a grand jury in Somerset County to stand trial for assault and battery.

It was during the mild winter of February 1929 that his older brother Dario made one of his rare trips to Cairnbrook. Dario was accompanied by one of the fellow musicians who played with him in a Philadelphia orchestra. In the early Spring, long after Dario had returned to his Philadelphia home and the night club circuit, strange accidents began to occur at or around the garage of that competitor for repair work. On separate occasions, a prized hunting dog was found dead, a car engine blew apart when started, the garage office was a smoldering shell after an unexplainable fire, and the garage owner was found mumbling and walking shoeless down a gravel trail about a mile distant.

Charges against Alfonso were dropped. In April, a mysterious box was found tucked under the towing boom extending from the Packard repair truck. At first suspicious of retribution, Alfonso laughed after he pried open the box with a crowbar while ducking behind the protection of a rear wheel and found a large wad of dollar bills held in a gold clip, a change bag filled with coins, and a 1914 pistol. The money totaled far more than had been lost in that incident from earlier in the year.

chapter eighteen

Most other matters of life had become routine business. Josephine continued to drive the school bus; her 1926 Diamond-T which she had dubbed the "Jitney," was replaced with a Reo, powered by a Buick motor and two transmissions that provided seven gear speeds to push through the mud trails and climb the Mountain Road. Open to the cab was a homemade 'cheese box,' with two bench seats extending lengthwise and glass windows covered by sliding wooden doors. Alfonso kept busy selling Buicks and providing repairs. He was troubled that the volume of work to keep the truck fleet in operation had increased dramatically.

Sam had signed a contract to truck coal from a mine in West Virginia to the depot in Central City. Alfonso was aghast. "The West Virginia coal is so easy to mine, it's practically laying on the top of the ground," Sam argued. "We can buy it cheap and sell it for a huge mark-up."

Sam confessed to having committed them to a limited partnership in the coal mine. He rationalized his decision by arguing that the trucks were set up to move coal and often missed out on return loads because the trucks were covered with too much coal dust. "If we set up a triangular circuit," he reasoned, "we guarantee ourselves full loads for two of the three legs of the trip."

The logic did little to convince Alfonso, but he was willing to acquiesce when Sam shared the numbers that promised a healthy income; if he had looked closer, Alfonso would have discovered that Sam greatly underestimated the outgo. They did make a generous amount of money at the beginning of the venture. The problems began to appear and widen in direct correlation to the potholes and divots that turned the access road to the mine into a quagmire. God damn mud. The trucks had to work in tandem teams to push or pull vehicles stuck in the mud or tow trucks to repair sites for broken axles, springs and wheels. Under the arrangement to which Sam had agreed, they were obligated to pay for the coal that was mined and staged for shipment at the mine site. Their trucking partnership was on the hook for all costs associated with transport. Despite his best efforts to remind Sam about the road-repair experience they had during the war, the lessons did not stick. Sam was creative and successful with the direction he provided to individual truckers, but he could not grasp the more expansive system management that was needed.

The pile of bills past due began to stack up in rhythm to the accumulation of cheap coal. When they eventually reached the point where the enterprise was losing money, Alfonso had to face the painful decision to walk away from the partnership. He patiently explained to Sam that the value of the entire collection of coal awaiting shipment was less than the amount of money they now owed. Initiating bankruptcy proceedings was the alternative recommended by Mr. Brant; Alfonso resisted because the money was owed to a number of vendors that also served the garage repair and car sales activities. He had advised Sam to negotiate a settlement with the coal company or find a broker who could resell the stack of coal.

ALFONSO WAS NOT SURPRISED WHEN THE BANK TELLER ASKED HIM to take a seat in the waiting area; Mr. Brant would like to meet with him. Alfonso was a bit miffed that the clerk refused to take his money deposits from the garage, nor process payments loans from the credit line, deferring all transactions to Mr. Brant.

"There was no way to stop him," Mr. Brant said hurriedly as he rushed into the bank and pulled Alfonso into his office, but not before locking the doors, pulling the shades and placing the closed sign in the window.

"What are you talking about?" Alfonso asked.

"Your trucking fleet account. Sam has vastly overspent from the account; here is a stack of bank overdrafts. This morning I froze the account, but the damage is done."

Alfonso was stunned by the pronouncement. His stomach began to sink as he recalled the inventory of new parts that had been gradually shifted from the Cairnbrook truck depot to the repair site near the mine. The operable trucks in the reserve fleet also had been moved. The more that Alfonso thought about it, the more he realized that all that remained of the trucking operation in Cairnbrook was used parts and debris.

"The news is worse," Brant continued. "I just came from a meeting at the National Bank in Central City. They have agreed to take over our accounts; we are closing our doors permanently. The rush began this morning as news spread of the stock market crash. As soon as I realized what Sam was doing, I closed your accounts," he continued as he slid an envelope of money across the desk.

Alfonso stared at the envelope with an extended trance. Mr. Brant feared he had once again reverted to a catatonic state in response to tragic news and was almost relieved when Alfonso quietly asked, "how much?"

"$743.35. All there in the envelope. You can count it out."

"No. How much do the overdrafts total?" Alfonso already knew to the penny how much money was in his accounts. With the weekly deposits in hand, he would be left with just under a thousand dollars. He almost responded with glee when he learned the amount was $292.10, but the slight smile turned into a grimace when he saw tears rolling along the creases that lined Mr. Brant's face.

"The 29th of October, 1929. The day it ends."

In later reflection Alfonso wished he had paid more attention to the last words he heard from Mr. Brant as the chair screeched in response to his movement to stand. He had no tears of his own. Not then, nor later at the funeral, attended by few, in reaction to the suicide.

Alfonso covered the overdrafts drawn on the bank, severed his partnership in the trucking fleet, and never again spoke to Sam.

⸺⸺⸺⸺

Events in Europe held scant attention for Alfonso. He had learned of the death of the Italian Senator Alessandro Chiappelli in 1931. Other information about family in Italy was scarce. Josephine had made sure that visits with Egisto were limited and mostly prefectural; Italian never was spoken in their household.

Every once in a while Alfonso would disappear on a hunting trip, always returning with a trophy. Stuffed deer heads replete with multi-pointed antlers and feet configured for clothes hooks decorated the garage office and new car showroom. Strings of fish would feed the entire street. Never once did Alfonso take any of his sons with him on his hunting or fishing trips. In fact, not a single photograph can be found that pictures Alfonso with any of his children. There are several rare photos of Josephine and Alfonso sitting together, but not until they had advanced in age.

In the late days of March 1932 the *Philadelphia Inquirer* reported that the police had taken Dario Chiappelli into questioning regarding the 1 March 1932 kidnapping of the Charles Lindbergh baby; a car registered in his name had been spotted near the Lindbergh home. The incident never was mentioned by Alfonso. Josephine, remembering that her husband was away on a hunting trip that first week of March, likewise never mentioned the incident, although for the remaining years of her life she maintained a scrapbook of newspaper clippings that followed the ongoing details of the Lindbergh kidnapping.

The economies of scale disappeared with the death of Dr. McMains in 1934. New car sales had virtually disappeared. Alfonso shifted his new car sales to Dodge trucks and Plymouth models which were more affordable for his target audience.

As the business reduced in response to the suppressed demand for services, a pattern developed for Alfonso and Josephine that would vary slightly for their remaining years. Alfonso served in a variety of civic duties. He was a founding member of the local American Legion post and served a tour as commander. He never went to church although the weekly donation from Cairnbrook Garage, deposited in the collection envelope by Josephine, always neared the top of the contribution list for St. John the Baptist Catholic Church. Generous donations routinely were made to Boys Town and in support of American Indians. 'Oh boo-ba-boo' were the words most often heard from Alfonso.

Josephine hovered over her three sons with a heavy hand and an exhausting string of corrective words. She was short on her praise, long with her lectures, and quick with the stick. Raymond was a rather docile child; his slow development following his premature birth was further delayed with a case of rheumatic fever. Richard was the polar opposite in most traits. Whereas Raymond was sedate and cautious, Richard explored with reckless abandon, pushing the limits in all manners of behavior and often earning the strap from his mother. Ralph was the charmer; he quickly learned that if he stayed within her bounds of control his mother would reward him with treats and toys. The brothers each became altar boys for the Catholic Church, which bound their weekends with catechism classes on Saturdays and church services on Sundays. Weekdays were busy with school work, and whatever free time they might have had was consumed with assigned duties at home or at the Cairnbrook Garage.

"This will all be yours someday," Josephine would often press in demanding that her sons attend to services provided at the Cairnbrook Garage.

The years progressively advanced the role each of those sons would play. Raymond mostly was engaged in the administrative aspects of the business, with Richard mastering the mechanics; the brains and the brawn, some would say. Their cumulative work began to displace Josephine, allowing her to turn more attention to other tasks. Ralph kept out of the way by starting his own business; he opened a bicycle repair shop in a space he converted in the attic of the Garage.

Alfonso receded to the background in customer interactions as his sons stepped forward. The daylight hours found him in the quiet solitude of engine repair, where he could work with his tools and machines to provide the more refined details of 'wrenching' that only a seasoned mechanic could accomplish. The nighttime hours often found him seated at a card table contemplating his poker hand and nursing a beer. Alfonso listed his occupation as 'machinist' on census documents, reflecting his joy in an emerging entertainment in which he found a modicum of happiness—auto racing. Many of the local racers built their success on knowledge they were able to extract by studying how Alfonso built his engines.

Josephine insisted—and each son dutifully complied—that each be marked with an Ash cross on the forehead on the Wednesday of each year that began the period of Lent in the Catholic calendar. A poppy flower was pinned to the shirt of all family members on the 11th day of each November.

Josephine continued to hold affinity for her Slovak roots. She noted that when the German army invaded her Slovakian home-land, Adolph Hitler ordered that Gorals be treated like gypsies. The Gorals fought as partisan freedom fighters in the Tatra Mountains, which separated Oscadnica by about 25 miles from a Polish town that became known as Auschwitz.

The American entry into the war arrived with the teenage years for Raymond, Richard, and Ralph. Raymond dropped to his knees in the middle of the Forbes Road fronting the garage, literally crying in protest that his application to serve in the military was denied because of his history of poor health. The disqualifier was rheumatic heart resulting from his childhood fever. The relief Josephine felt on this count again was offset by Richard whose enlistment in the Army placed him in the Pacific Theater where he trained for the invasion of Okinawa.

During fire-fighting training an instructor with a beef against Richard (he said Richard was too happy) cut off the water supply. The building collapsed on Richard and a wooden beam crushed into his face severely burning his nose. Josephine fainted when she heard the news. Richard carried the scars of a disfiguration until the latter part of his life when he had a plastic surgeon reconstruct his face. The physician said when he cut open the nose he found fragments of carbonated wood still embedded. Richard also came back from the war with tattoos; he had an eagle sketched across his chest and a dancing girl on his shoulder.

In 1960, Richard accepted a contract to provide emergency road services for a section of the Pennsylvania Turnpike. The turnpike, built on an abandoned railroad, provided 360 miles of limited-access highway that extended east-to-west to span the entire state. Richard remembered his father speaking praise for the 'Voie Sacree,' the road that was essential during the war.

Richard adopted a habit of investing in oil paintings. He bought paintings by the inch; that is in stacks, an inch at a time. He had thousands of paintings, mostly from artists who were listed in the art associations of Europe and were struggling to reestablish the arts in the aftermath of WWII. This was his gamble. He claimed the collection could be worth millions, but he confessed that he never paid more than $20 for a single painting. Richard often selected paintings for his art collection based on his preferences for shapes and shading; his preferences were driven by an interesting nuance—he was color blind. At one time he owned the world's largest collection of paintings from the well-regarded Italian artist Lucio Ranucci.

IN 1949, ALFONSO AND JOSEPHINE BUILT A NEW BRICK HOUSE on the used-car sales lot adjacent to Cairnbrook Garage, using, in part, funds that had been promised to veterans of the Great War; there they lived their remaining years. In those post-war years,

Alfonso routinely sent money to relatives in Italy and offered to sponsor their emigration to America; all relatives remained in Europe.

Josephine was steadfast in a routine that began daily at 0600. On school days she would be opening the doors to the bus-barn by 0700—earlier if snow was dribbling on the roads. She adopted a vested interest in each student assigned to her bus. Included in her routine was the preparation of sandwiches which she would pack into individual paper bags along with a piece of fruit and occasionally a piece of chocolate. Josephine had observed too many children stepping onto her bus without a mid-day meal; she would not let any student leave her bus without a snack. A box behind the driver's seat was a permanent fixture, always stocked with hats, gloves, and jackets for those in need.

The comingled coal towns of Cairnbrook and Central City had grown to a population exceeding 5,000, supporting 17 churches and 21 bars. Three red-brick elementary schools fed an expansive high school that featured a modern basketball court and a brightly-lit football field. The coal company was generous in maintaining an expansive community park that included a baseball stadium, swimming pool, and community center.

The mines closed in 1958, signaling a rapid demise of Cairnbrook. The coal mine village that had grown to become the fourth largest city in the county now was abandoned to the winds that drift all immigrants into the breathe and breadth of America. That same year, Alfonso suffered a massive heart attack. His daily habit of smoking a half-dozen City Club cigars and drinking an equal number of Black Label beers most likely contributed to the insult on his health.

Lacking private health insurance, Alfonso was admitted to the newly opened hospital operated by the Veteran's Administration in Butler, Pennsylvania, for a period of rehabilitation. His days in managing the Cairnbrook Garage came to an end.

"Time to let go," Josephine concluded without room for disagreement. "We made our fortune; give the boys a chance to earn their own way."

Alfonso became a fixture seated on his front porch watching for cars to pull up to the gas pumps. Although he surrendered control of the business management, his quiet presence and scent of his cigar was constant.

The absence of civic leadership became evident after the mine closures removed management from providing oversight for the community development. The remaining population coalesced into factions of groups who were loud on demanding what others should do, but silent on how resources of money and manpower would be provided. Years of mismanagement and neglect took their toll, beginning with a fire that destroyed the baseball stadium. The concrete in the swimming pool began to crack and the pump failed to provide enough water; eventually the pool was filled with dirt and paved over for a tennis court. The community center slowly dissolved from the rainwater seeping through a myriad of holes in the roof. A 4th of July celebration by a group of youngsters sent an explosion of sparks into the building; members of the fire company stood by and watched the building burn to the ground because there was not enough of the structure sound enough to save.

The community that had been built on an American model of corporate prosperity had become a disposable unit.

Alfonso died on 10 October 1975, age 80.

⁓⁓⁓

JOSEPHINE FILLED HER WIDOW YEARS WITH AN EVOLVING LIST of interests and activities, creating a workshop in her basement for carpet weaving, furniture upholstering, sewing blankets, and other household projects. She continued to drive her school bus until age 75. The next year she was involved in her first and only automotive accident; her driving days were over. The year following, Josephine suffered a stroke that divided her body in half with paralysis; extended periods of physical rehabilitation achieved modest restoration of movement. Josephine lingered with inactivity, dying on 24 Jan 1986 at age 80.

In a eulogy at her funeral, a grandson reflected that the only time he ever saw Josephine get visibly angry with him was the day he said "I love you, grandma."

"Love gets you nothing," she had said in sharp notation, he reported. "Love will not put food on the table. Never say that again."

In later years, Raymond operated a gas station and managed several school bus routes; he died of early-onset Alzheimer's disease in 1986 at age 61. Richard began his working days providing long-distant hauling up and down the East Coast before accepting the contract to provide towing and emergency services in support of a large section of the Pennsylvania Turnpike. Ralph took over management of the Cairnbrook Garage and operated the business until its closure with his retirement in 1991; by then the coal town had disintegrated into a slum. With poverty and neglect now commanding the Appalachian coal fields, Cairnbrook no longer provided an embrace of community nor collective of family.

Chiappelli is the name of a family that originated in an Etruscan culture, survived one thousand years of Roman rule and provided a storied presence within an Italian region for another thousand years before emerging as an American saga. The name is destined to serve one thousand years in the American culture, with the Etruscan influence living on in Chiappelli grandchildren and great-grandchildren who number in the professional ranks of physicians, college professors, business leaders, lawyers, engineers, teachers, nurses, and writers.

Chiappelli now is an American name.

The Door Down

by Cinda McClure Gibbon

*"Rescue crews are working
feverishly tonight to reach forty-five
coal miners who were trapped in Mine18
of the Barnes &Tucker Co. at Shanktown,
[Indiana County, Pennsylvania] fifteen miles
northeast of this place, by a gas explosion
this afternoon at 3:30 o'clock."*

"Mine Blast Traps 45 in Pennsylvania."
New York Times. January 26, 1924

Introductory Note

The trail of common interests and the steps of research led to the home of a second cousin, Cinda McClure Gibbon. Cinda was piecing together the story of her own grandfather, Pio Chiappelli, the youngest brother of Alfonso. This short story, *The Door Down*, presents the research notes and story segments that Cinda had gathered while struggling with a chronic medical condition that claimed her life on 18 Jun 2018.

Something Real

unt Bruna asked if I was going to the Chiappelli family reunion in August, and I said I supposed I would, though I thought it strange for her to ask nearly eight months ahead. After a pause, she drawled, "Well, it starts the balls rolling in my mind. I want to say something about my father. I think I might have a thing or two to say." I waited while she examined the hills. I knew it wasn't up for discussion whether or not she had something to say.

The drive between Adams County and Indiana County was a convenience. I visited my parents who lived forty minutes from my aunt, and she visited her son who lived forty minutes from me. The drive was three hours long and for most of it Bruna talked—about church, Frank, Tony, families, neighbors—so I listened to her or to static punctuated radio and counted dead deer.

"Oh, if I could only get some things to verify what I remember about the mine explosion when I was a little girl." Again she stopped. She was waiting for me to offer to do something. When I was a child, she never hesitated to assign me a task, but now that I was a woman with a husband, three children, and a full time job…she knew she was crossing the line. I tallied another deer with its head bent backward over its spine, its pink tongue a bright loll on its black lips.

"What kinds of things do you want?" I was stalling.

She shot me a look; she knew I was stalling. "Well there is a man in Clymer by the name of John Busovicki and he shares his postcards and old pictures with the newspaper. I was talking to your mother and she thought I should call him. So I went over to the telephone book, turned to the Bs in the telephone book, and mercy me! The page of the Bs that I needed—? That page was torn out! So I had to borrow the neighbor's book."

"Hmmm," I hummed, sounding sympathetic.

She shrugged her shoulders, then threw her hands, palms out with a wrist flick, which meant "Would you believe it?" or "It's always something." She was telling it funny to loosen me up.

"So finally I called and introduced myself. I didn't want to waste his time so right off the bat, I got around to the Shanktown explosion. I told him I was only a little girl and I just wanted something that I remembered verified. I told him that we lived next to a big bony pile." Aunt Bruna put one hand on the dash to steady herself as she shifted to face me. "Do you know what a bony pile is?"

I glanced at the guardrail and then at Aunt Bruna. "Yeah, sure, it's a big pile of slag that was separated from the coal. Mom didn't let us go down there."

"And a good thing she didn't, I'll tell you! Bony piles will swallow you whole!" Aunt Bruna lifted her right hand and chopped it down. She crossed her arms and let her head drop. There was a long pause.

"What did Mr. Busovicki say?" I prompted.

She startled, then rubbed her right temple. "Yes, well, I told him I needed a picture. And he sent me some good pictures and some newspaper articles about the old mine. I have it all right here." Aunt Bruna bent over struggling against her seat belt, and reached inside her pocketbook. Finally she pulled out a bulky yellow mailing envelope. She grunted with the effort of it and exhaled in a whoo as she straightened. "I made a cassette tape in there too. You listen to it."

"And then what?"

"What do you think? You're in a school all day, there's a library there. Of all things…." I stumbled to agree but it wasn't fast enough.

"Well, am I right?" Her patience with me was done. I was being childish; I should have already offered to help. "I want a list that shows my father, your grandfather, was a survivor of that explosion."

"But why? We know he —."

"I want to prove it was true! It's more than just some story, you know!"

I knew better than to ask again, so I let it drop.

Bruna Chiappelli Landucci, tape transcription 1996

It was a few weeks ago; yes, all day that day I had an urge to go to Star-ford. That's the name of Shanktown now, they call it Starford. I don't know what the urge was, but I just wanted to go through there again.

I had a church friend drive me and there it was, you know, just like in Mr. Busovicki's picture. That was something I'll tell you. Oh, and I wanted to read some of these articles for you... . This one is from the Indiana County paper called the, Indiana Evening Gazette, and it's dated Monday, January 28, 1924.

'As they penetrated the workings the rescue parties recon-structed a scene when the explosion occurred at a point near the No. 7 right heading.'

You may not know about a heading. It's like a hallway off the main line, and the main line connects all those headings to the surface.

'John Yendler met the explosion full face. Yendler was blown the length of 14 cars and decapitated.'

[I turned off the tape recorder because the kids were in the room. I must have been sufficiently nonchalant because none of them noticed when I relocated.]

'The cars were piled, and all brattices and doors had been blown away and the gas left free to circulate.'

Well, that touches a memory, I'll tell you. Brattices are the...oh, what-do-you-call-them? The partitions! That's right! They used to hang them like curtains on the columns in the mine and that's the way they would control the airflow in the mines, to make sure there was fresh air to breathe, and to help vent the gas you see.

And you would say what would a woman of seventy-seven

years know about brattices? Well mining played a big part in my life. My husband, Anthony Robert Landucci, he used to work as a miner. And you know he studied that mining law till he knew it by heart. He'd recite it, and I couldn't help but learn it too. And my husband admired Jerome Croyle which I think was a boss there at the time. And when we had our first child, well, we lost our first child, but when our second child was born we named him Jerome Anthony after Mr. Croyle. We call him Tony though. And then later when I had our other son, Francis Keenan was an inspector at that time, and we named him after Mr. Keenan, but we call him Franco. So you can see both of my sons, my husband, my father, and my brother—there's always something about the mines in their lives. 'Course today they're not miners. They have their own businesses. I wanted them both to do something real like be a plumber or an electrician, but they had their own ideas. There's a story about each one though the boys never liked to hear me talking about them; they say that I "embellish" which is just not true if that's how I remember it.

But back to brattices and airflow in the mines because of my father, Pio Chiappelli, your grandfather and it's the explosion I want you to look up for me.

RESEARCH

"You dreamed dreams of what America was to be, and I hope you brought the dreams with you…. Just because you brought dreams with you, America is more likely to realize the dreams such as you brought. You are enriching us if you came expecting us to be better…."

—Woodrow Wilson, in a speech given to a group of naturalized Americans in Philadelphia, May 10, 1915

"In PA, 55.4% of laborers were foreign born."

"Little training [of a new employee was] done by the company, a new man starts as a helper, and picks up the trade almost entirely from his buddy or from other miners.… This opportunity to work in a relatively independent position appeals because it enables the foreigner…to escape some of the handicaps of discrimination."

"After the coal is broken it is ready to be shoveled into the mine cars.…The miners are supposed to remove all large pieces of rock, slate, and other foreign material from the coal. In addition to drilling, shooting, and loading, the miner must perform a variety of other tasks in his room [that] are usually referred to as "dead work." The track must be laid, timber must be unloaded and props set to support the roof. If the roof caves in, the rock must be removed. Wrecked cars must be put back on the track. If there is water in the room, it must be bailed or pumped out. If there is gas in the room, brattice work may be required. A miner may be paid for some of this "dead work," or it may be done by "company men." But…the miner is responsible for the work in his room."

—Morris, Homer Lawrence.
The Plight of the Bituminous Coal Miner.
Philadelphia: University of Pennsylvania Press, 1934.

Pio and his buddy, Pietro Corsini, knelt to swing picks in short arcs, undercutting the coal seam. The coal chipped away in spits of grit and brick-sized chunks. (Don Giovanni mocked the wooden supports overhead, but Pio was sure they were fine.) Cold and stony, the ground was uncomfortable even through two layers of pants. Saturday—not a normal workday—and there was no money for this deadwork, but, they worked to prepare for Monday. Paychecks were measured by the weight of coal in the cars.

The glow of their safety lamps reflected in the broken angles of coal. Pio hummed for a bit. For swinging picks, he especially liked the slow staccato build of "La calunnia è un venticello" from Barbiere Di Siviglia. It was the opera he knew best; the first one he remembered. As a boy he had seen a free dress rehearsal. Later, he himself had sung in the chorus at the Politeama Mabellini. In Italy, he could work all day as a smith and sing in the opera chorus at night. Here in America, it was only the strong back, but still, he sang. He practiced in a heading after a shift, warming up with scales until his stomach tensed at the end of his breath.

Pio stopped at the end of the song because it was more important to listen to Don Giovanni. Fear was part of the job; and Don Giovanni was the voice of his fear. He liked the joke of the proud opera character being assigned in hell to watch over poor married coal miners with not a woman in sight. Pio and Pietro never spoke of fear, not at work or at home; none did. But it was unwise not to have it.

Fear could keep you alive. Unlike Pietro who prayed regularly under his breath, Pio entertained himself with Don Giovanni—who mocked him. *A rich irony!* he'd laugh, *here you are, knees to your nose, and the other roof could fall. Then where would you be? Trapped under the four feet of coal you were trying to drop. He-heh!*

But Pio knew the room's sandstone roof would rip or pop before a fall, giving them some time to run. The props holding the coal above them would split or crack. If they hit gas, a very small amount would make the lamp flicker or change color, or they might notice that they were winded or dizzy. But not even Don Giovanni would have time to shout if they opened a pocket. If he still prayed, he would have, but for now, there was the Don.

Hours passed with just the chink, chink of the picks. They slowly picked out the rubble below the seam, with breaks to listen and look. They could sometimes hear the mining machine working two headings down, connecting it back to the main slope. Kelly was the cutter today and Parkins the scraper. Superintendent, John Stone would be there. The foreman, Stoker, was down the same heading, but in a different room with the other machine. Pio didn't like the machines—too loud, too much dust—but sometimes the sliding note of the machine's whine made him think of a song or a bit of coloratura, one he might have forgotten otherwise.

Pio had worked with Pietro Corsini since before the war. Pietro, Pio, and Pio's wife, Elisa Gianni, came from Villa de Cireglio, a small village just north of Pistoia in Toscana—they were paisani. But Pio told anyone who asked that he was born in Udine, far to the north-east. Even his children. Pio had never told the officials his true place of birth. The draft had been after him—the military got his brother 'Berto. Pio had a picture of him so handsome in his mustache and uniform that Pio could almost imagine that 'Berto had been happy about it. However Pio got out before they conscripted him. He might still be wanted for draft evasion for all he knew.

They stopped for a bite. No midday in the mines, just hunger or a good stopping point in the work could mean lunch. While they ate, Pietro gossiped. A man in Nanty-Glo left a wife and six children. He was an educated man, had studied piano and violin in a monastery in Germany. But just last week, he never went to work; never went home. One piece of luck was the oldest boy was fifteen, old enough to take up the trade. It was a shame on the family though, just the same. Pio nodded; he knew the man, George was his name.

When their mine had no work, Pio and Pietro rode the coal trains of the Pennsylvania Railroad to the town, Nanty-Glo, nearly twenty miles south. Pietro had a cousin in the union there; it was easy to be hired for a day. Pio met George after a shift when every-one was black with coal. He said Pio could be Othello. Pio asked, "Verdi's or Rossini's?"

"So you are the one I've heard of," George whooped. Talking about opera had made Pio's pulse race a little, gave him energy— even at the end of a shift. Pio and Pietro had a drink from George's flask under the railway bridge while they waited. It had good acoustics, and Pio sang for George; Pietro clapped to keep time. Pio had seen him again a month ago, but only for a few sentences. George heard about a hotel in Pittsburgh, the Anderson, where they hired musicians. George said he was going; that he couldn't bear the mines any more—not even for the sake of his family. George asked Pio to come with him. Pio hadn't given him an answer; he needed to think about it. Furthermore Pio had not told Pietro. No one could know where he was heading, not Pietro, not his brother Egisto, or his sister, Rosina, who had married a Venturini from the Villa before emigrating to Western Pennsylvania.

Pio thought of his son's laughing face, the way he'd look back with mischief while running. Carlo was ten. He was above ground right now, working in the chutes, picking slate from the coal. He was too young to go underground. Too young to be a nipper, and such a dreamer! Just like Elisa! He'd miss when he should open the doors for the coal cars. He could be caught by the speed of their opening arc. Legs or hips were crushed that way, pinning boys to the walls. And beside his worries there was practicality. In Pittsburgh, it was only the *calabresi*, Italians from the south of Italy. He knew no names for introductions.

STUCK TOGETHER

I had asked once why we weren't Catholic since I knew that Nonna kept a rosary in her apron pocket; Mom said it was because of one of Nonno's twin sisters. Back in Italy, Nonno had twin sisters six years older than himself, Maria and Nazarena. They could sing as well as he could, but only Nonno sang in an opera chorus. Maria married well, but Nazarena married a *bruto* who beat her.

Nazarena came home on a day when Nonno was there; she was bruised and bloody. In a rage, Nonno brought her to the church. "She hung like a rag doll." He begged the priest to release her from the marriage, but the priest said that marriage was a sacrament. Nonno raged and "he spat on the shoe of the priest," and "never darkened the door of a church again. The rag doll seemed like filigree as Nonno would have little experience with rag dolls but the very specific placement of the spit, and the fact that the story portrayed Nonno scandalously made me believe it was true.

Stories that began with "back in Italy" were retold at holidays. Like the liturgy, the stories went with certain holidays; "The Shoe of the Priest" was always told at Easter. I didn't know if the event had happened at that time of year or if the blasphemy made the best counterpoint with Easter and so got a bigger laugh. When I asked questions about family stories, I was chastened. I had "big ears" or a "big nose"—either meant I was involving myself in something that was none of my business. I wasn't allowed to question a story's details too closely. Consequently I looked for odd images or scraps of angry dialogue that when re-told, were presented as a funny story—both were measures by which I determined "the truth."

Funerals were so annual in my childhood that one may well have counted them a holiday analogous to Easter or Halloween. The funerals began when I was five with Uncle Tony, Aunt Bruna's husband, who I don't remember at all. Aunt Eva died when I was nine, who I remember very well. She had two sons but everyone said I should have been her daughter—we looked so alike. Hodgkins Disease, seeded by her days as Rosie the Riveter in a Pittsburgh steel yard in World War II, blossomed in her, turning as yellow as zinnias in her back yard. It was in the back seat on the way to her funeral I was given one of her hats to wear. I was gooning around with it until I saw my face in the rear view mirror and spooked. For the first time I realized everyone I loved would grow old or sick and die. That I would die. When I was sixteen and tearfully driving home to make curfew, Eva's face appeared in the traffic light, bright-framed in sparker-fire, and comforting. At family gatherings for all my years, her oldest son takes my picture, panning my face for hers.

Nonno died when I was seven. His hands were hard, and I loved the smell of his pipe smoke. I was sent to sit with him on the couch while we waited for Sunday lunch. He sang till it was ready, teaching me the names of the operas—the *Barber of Seville*. I loved Figaro's aria; Nonno punctuated the phrasing by tickling me. *Nabucco*, and the bad man—*Don Giovonni*. Nonno wouldn't sing Tosca anymore because I kept asking him why she jumped off the cliff. *Orfeo e Euridice* was my favorite because it seemed like just the kind of trick that someone would play on you at school. (*Nyah! Nyah! Made you look!*) I asked Nonno where was Hades, and he was quiet for a moment and just when I was getting the tingles, he said, "Ah bellina, it is far far below."

"Below the coal mine?" I was incredulous.

"Si, Si, below the coal, even below the Inferno!" He nearly shouted the last word—Dante was from Toscana, his name was invoked for the highest authority. I thought Nonna was pulling my leg, so I thought hard.

"Then how did Ofeo find it?," I thought myself sly.

"Bellina, Bellina…you must never never go, just like the bony piles. Ofeo, brave Ofeo! He took," he paused for effect, "He took the door under the mountain." His voice descrendoed to a wavering whisper. I was terrified.

The memory is slippery but I think that not long afterward, I saw *The Pied Piper of Hamlin* on television. When the Piper is paid to pipe away the rats that infest Hamlin, the music he plays is Edvard Grieg's *In the Hall of the Mountain King*. The music also attracts Hamlin's children, and mesmerized they follow, oblivious to their parents' calling. And then a shock of recognition—a door slid open in the mountain to a path leading down, down. Ever afterward I would peer through the back seat window looking for the door, invariably making myself carsick.

After Nonno died and the diabetes took Nonna's legs, we went to Aunt Bruna's on Sundays so she could go to three or four hours of church. The four of us—Mom and we three girls—entered Aunt Bruna's house through the storefront. She always asked us, "Hungry?" but never waited for an answer. She had the salami ready and sliced twice. She rolled the two slices in a tube and held them up to her eyes as if to look through—an old joke needing no comment.

Once we had greeted Nonna, Bruna would pick up her purse and Bible from the kitchen table and ask Sharon and me, "Coming?" We went with her to Sunday School, that is if Mom or Nonna didn't mind, or if Aunt Bruna didn't have a chore for us.

In the winter, I held my breath till Nonna released us from knitting and crocheting lessons. I dreaded knitting because Nonna taught by tolerating no mistakes. She kept a knitting needle in her hand, and rapped our knuckles for a stitch too tight or too loose. I had to count the stitches after each row.

Every skill or chore I learned from the Chiappelli women had to be done just so, as an amulet against bad luck or harm. It was important to do things right; doing things right could keep away the evil eye. I noticed that Uncle Carlo had an iron ball bearing in his pocket with a cord cross- wrapped around it; he said it was for the same thing. I told Aunt Bruna what he said and she threw her hands, sniffed, and said witheringly, "Leave it to Carlo.…"

RESEARCH

Accounts told of lynchings [of Italians] in Louisiana, Mississippi, Florida, Colorado, Kentucky, Illinois, Washington, and New York between the years of 1885 and 1915, some 50 killings in all.…a number of reasons [can be suggested] for the targeting of Italians. Economic hardship had caused a souring of attitudes toward the immigrants recruited as cheap labor for mines.… In many cases, Italians remained apart, choosing not to assimilate.……Italians were victimized, in part, because they weren't considered white.

—Pacchioli, David. "Dark Legacy."
Research/Penn State. May 2004, v.24, I.

"According to the National Coal Producers Assoc. 1924 was the worst period in coal industry since 1894-96. Causes were over-development and lack of demand. During this time of hardship, the KKK began to organize in PA. There were 125,000 Klansmen in PA by the end of 1924, and as many as 250,000 two years later. "

"1924 Columbus Day celebrations in Nanty-Glo were disrupted with a cross-burning. Miners suspected that management of the Heisley No. 3 mine in Nanty-Glo was sponsoring Klan activities."

—Michrina, Barry P. Pennsylvania.
Mining Families: the Search for Dignity in the Coalfields.
Lexington, KY: University Press of Kentucky, 1993.

PIO CHIAPPELLI, 1924

Sometimes at the end of a shift, when Pio turned down a heading to sing, Pietro joked that Pio chased the devil with the song. Others agreed; it was good luck to have Pio sing a tunnel. They needed some luck that winter. "Joe Poll," had quit the job in December saying the mine would kill them all. Joe Poll used to be Giuseppe Poli, but he'd changed it when he naturalized just after the war. They all had made good money during the war, inspiring many to naturalize. But the armistice left a surplus of coal, and work slumped. Pietro said that Joe was a lazy man, a drunkard who didn't care for his family, and what about his boy? What kind of example was quitting for little Joe? At ten-years-old, it would be soon time to take him in, teach him the trade. What future could there be for the boy if the father walked out?

Then talk turned to union gossip and Dominick Gelotte. Pietro heard that many in Nanty-Glo supported Gelotte over John Brophy to lead the union in District 2. Pio sniffed; Brophy had been president since 1916, and had been a miner in Nanty-Glo itself. He and Pietro read the education program. Brophy was a good man and well known nationally, though an adversary to the stronger John Lewis in the national union.

"Che cosa? Ti spia per Gelotte?," Pio teased. Some spied for Lewis in District 2, some for management. Good information could bring a man a bit of cash and good will perhaps. But it was a joke to think that Gelotte was influential enough to have a network of operatives.

"No. No. What do you think?" Pietro knew Gelotte's bid was unlikely; besides it wasn't Brophy who was the more immediate problem. Rumor had it that Heisley #3 in Nanty-Glo was full of the Klan.

"Gelotte is spreading a plan though. For the cattolicos." Pio waved, but Pietro continued. "It's a society against the Klan. A burning circle against their crosses, eh? He calls it the Society of the Burning Circle."

Pio hummed noncommittally. "A knife is better."

Sure, sure. But for everybody, right? Like the union. We'll see how they like having something burned at them. You see. They will have their crosses on one hill and we will have our circles on another. Like a big bright game of Tic-Tac-Toe up and down the hilltops! All of them!" They laughed a long one at that, Pio clapping Pietro's shoulder.

They talked on about Biamonte who had run for Prothonotary last year, but lost miserably. Neither Pio or Pietro had naturalized and so couldn't vote, but only Italians voted for either Gelotte or Biamonte. Pietro mused about naturalization for the right to vote. If Italianos stuck together, they could run the union, and maybe elect some county positions. And why not? There were as many Italians as *Americanos* here—not all paisani to be sure, but Italians just the same. In the old country, never would the *Toscani* stand with those from the *Mezzogiorno* but here in *l'america*, they were all one people. And if they could elect Biamonte, then why not Gelotte, and why not the One Big Union, and then even the socialist, Smith, for President? Not Italian, but he was *cattolico*.

Pio snorted, Biamonte would be nobody without his brother Giuseppe's store money—and a *calabresi* besides. Gelotte winning meant Brophy losing, and Brophy was the only one who could stop the trouble caused by these *clamoroso*, the Klan.

Pietro went on to observe that according to his brother's letters, the Socialists here were holding up better than the workers' unions in *Toscana*. There, it was the *fascistas* and the *agrari*, the landlords that made the rules; here it was the coal and iron police, the owners, and even the judges. Union men here were called "Bolsheviks," and that Judge Langham in the big town—Indiana—had even outlawed the right to strike. That's why Pio thought Pietro was wrong; no union or society could win. Money made the say-so.

A few minutes pause and Pietro said he wanted to catch a short nap, *solo cinque minuti*. That was Pio's cue to sing a bit so Pietro could drop off. He selected "Va Pensiero" from Nabucco by Verdi—one of the few arias sung by the chorus without a soloist. The vocal range was right, dramatic baritone, and the Tessitura went only to E4. The last stanza was appropriate for a lullaby:

Va' pensiero sull'ali dorate
Attraversa le montagne e vola
Sugli oceani.
Raggiungi la terra, trova il luogo
Dove vanno tutti i bambini
Ogni notte dopo aver sentito questa ninna nanna.
Fly, thought, on wings of gold
Cross the mountains and fly
Over the oceans.
Reach the land find the place
Where all children go
Every night after listening to this lullaby.

More important than being a lullaby it was about yearning. The Hebrew slaves in the opera longed for their homeland and likewise most Italians he knew were homesick. Pio himself didn't care as much about Italy, but opera? He missed it with all his heart.

He remembered the song easily, it was one of his first experiences in a chorus at the Teatro Manzoni, over Christmas in 1901. Oreste Benedetti played Nabucco, the Babylonian king who prays to God for healing. Pio looked around the "room," so short they couldn't stand their full height and with a seam of coal—four feet high and twenty feet long between the side supports or pillars. In his mind the light refracted in the coalface became the lamps at the edge of the stage. Pio imagined the other voices in the chorus as he sang; he always stood by silver-haired Mario Pistolozzi. He imagined the heat of the stage lamps warming his face.

BRUNA CHIAPPELLI LANDUCCI, TAPE TRANSCRIPTION, 1996

Now this same article here says that the mine was worked by the aliens, but immigrants are what they mean, and it says that the people from Shanktown were silent as they waited for news. Well, we were just scared is all and nobody talked in front of strangers. It was bad times for immigrants. Most Americans didn't like immigrants, but I remember that Daddy thought a few neighbors were fine. I remember Daddy saying that he liked the names of Mr. Sickenberger's daughters, Alma and Blanche. And then he would laugh and say that those two girls were as pale as their names! Daddy said that was why he picked out my name. Bruna—it means "dark hair" in Italian, you know, like the word "brunette."

Now it was Italian custom to name the first boy after the father's father—which they did, Carlo was Daddy's Babbo's name—and the first girl after the mother's mother. So I should have been named Zelinda, but I was born with such thick dark hair. Well he chose the name Bruna. I wonder if they had a fight about that? After all it was your Nonna's mother that he skipped over. [Humph] Now what was I talking about before?

Oh yes the other immigrants besides Italians. Mr. Sickenberger yes; he died in that mine you know. I wonder what ever happened to his daughters....But anyway! For the other kinds—now Daddy had no trouble with the Slovaks and Slovenians. The neighbors next door, the Hudak's, they were Slovak and they were good people. But the Ukrainians! We were supposed to stay away from them.

Now I don't remember this but they told the story about the strike two years before the explosion when the company had wanted to lower wages; they said too much coal was driving down the price. So it was the union against the strikebreakers again. The strikebreakers are the ones that would cross the union picket lines to work the mines when the union wouldn't. If you did that, buddy, you better plan on leaving town and soon.

Many immigrants came out for the union and they walked from town to town to organize. The strike lasted a couple of months but in Windber, the strike dragged on and no wonder. A company man driving strikebreakers through a crowd hit and killed a miner's child. Now I'm sure it was an accident but it got the crowd in a uproar and they attacked the car, and the constables —the coal and iron police, constables was what we called them— well they beat the crowd which was mainly women and children with sticks. And here's where the Ukrainians come in, some said Ukrainians got them back with knives in the night. Daddy said, "Certo. Un occhio per un occhio."—an eye for an eye—but we were to stay away just the same!

So it was bad on immigrants if they worked any of the few jobs. Worse on Italians and any other Catholics. Daddy knew that Mama kept her rosary in her pocket, but he had all of us shaking in our boots at just the mention of the Coal and Iron police. We stuck together I'll tell ya. He made sure of that.

RESEARCH

About 3:00 pm January 26, 1924, when the explosion happened there were 47 men in the mine; 36 were killed and 11 escaped unhurt. The explosion originated at an air course face, where a "Flameproof" mining machine ignited gas. The ventilation of the advanced face was makeshift and irregular, and the cover of the rheostat on the machine was loosely bolted and part of the gasket missing; arcing was evident. The explosion fed by coal dust, extended into the neighboring set of entries and up the [mine's] slope.... Twelve men went to the main slope and died there. All

213

of the men in the gassy sections beyond the 6th right heading were killed where they were; the others died of the afterdamp.

—Shanktown, PA *Coal Dust Explosion,*
The Associated Press, January 1924

Fewer men than usual were working in the mine at the time or the death list would have been much more. All but a few of the victims were married men and leave families, 110 children being left fatherless.

—"Thirty-Six Miners Killed in Horrible Explosion." *The Journal,* Nanty-Glo, PA Thursday, January 31, 1924

PIO CHIAPPELLI, 1924

Pio joked that his forearms had become pick handles; if he could make his fingers into a pick head, then he'd be in the business. They had worked nearly the whole day to drop the coal. It was a good room—a four or five foot seam off the No. 6 left heading. The bosso, Stone, had assigned it, despite the grumbling of the new fireboss, Donahue. Times were so bad that even a preacher worked in this mine, though Pio noticed he didn't work today, no surprise as the weather was bitter cold, and the preacher had a long walk.

Donahue, had been through today at noon for the gas check, but they hadn't seen him since. Donahue bragged that he'd sent a letter to the Secretary of Labor to tell him that an Italian was to blame for the Spangler accident two years back. Pio and Pietro called him *Donna Uovo* or "Lady Egg." It was hard to pronounce these *la'mericano* names, because so many were not. Donahue was an Irishman but his name in Italian sounded immediately like mockery, which they were happy to apply. They assumed he was in the Klan. Pio's eldest brother, Egisto, said there were klaverns in Center Township too, and even Klan soldiers.

Finally they had picked out the entire depth of the seam. If they stretched, just their knees and feet would be left outside the coal.

214

They wriggled out, slowly stood, shrugging their shoulders. Then Pio crouched to drill the shot into the coalface, tilting up. Pietro —"Pete" is what Stone called him— laid the wires, packed the hole with twelve inches of black powder, and tamped it with dirt. They would shoot the coal down and go home, loading it later for a big-money Monday.

They had planned well. If the powder didn't blow, Stone—il bosso—said they must go home. A man could lose an eye and worse if he tried to re-set it. A man just over the border in the next county was killed that way. Another reason to stop was that fumes from the powder lingered after a shot, so if they stayed, they'd have to waste time fanning it out with their shovels. If they left it, the vents and fans would take care of it.

What's more, the union's check-weigh man wasn't working today—not a good day to load coal. The company men were not to be trusted with the weigh-in. Two strikes since the war had nearly broken the union; many mines were open shop now. This mine still held for the union, but the company had changed. They'd been working only five weeks for Lancashire, who had taken over from Glenside. Lancashire was a Barnes & Tucker mine. They had enough money to keep the mine up. Good luck for them.

But even if they couldn't trust the company to pay fairly, it was the company's job to keep the mine as safe as they could. No. 7 Right Flat, the next heading down from theirs, was why Pio and Pietro wore safety lamps now. It was hollowed out from an accidental explosion two years. Pio liked the acoustics of it now and often sang there after a shift.

Before that explosion, the heading hadn't been worked for months. To get it ready, men were hanging canvas to pump the gas—but they were working with open lamps, and she lit.

The mine inspector, Tom Loather, made a list of the dead and how they died: an explosion of gas resulting in loss of air, crushed by roof-falls, electrocuted, all were burnt to some degree. He came up from Indiana, walked around a few days with three other men, and posted rules before leaving.

1st. That all portions of the mine be examined by fire bosses regularly.

2nd. That all portions of the mine inside of No. 5 left and No. 6 right entries are worked exclusively with locked safety lamps.

3rd. That a suitable danger station with an attendant on duty at all times during working hours, day and night, to prevent the carrying of open lights or smokers into that portion of the mine.

Luckily the explosion had been small: no company property damaged. Explosions were to be expected. All mines had gas; fire-bases reported gas at nearly every heading in this one. Lucky she wasn't dusty. Coal dust could make a blast worse, taking fire and concussion through the air. Men said lit coal dust made the air look like thousands of matches struck at the same time.

More safety regulations required them to set the fuse outside their room, and then Donahue as the fireboss had to check it before they called "fire in the hole." (Don Giovanni barked one heh at Donna Uovo determining the safety of the fuse and powder.) They rolled out the wire, securing it with rocks.

Suddenly, the floor bucked; a roar louder than their ears could hear threw Pietro back into Pio and slammed them against the coalface. Pio saw flames in his mind before he blacked out, the coalface scraping his head and back. Pio's head rang with the impact, and he blacked out. He was immediately dreaming.

The actress playing Tosca stepped downstage, her skin rosy in the footlights. "Vissi d'arte, vissi d'amore." I lived for art, I lived for love." The shell of the stage in Teatro Manzoni curved for amplification. He could almost see the notes curl off that curve and rise, as buoyant as a bubble. Her vibrato spun and resonated even after she released the note, magically harmonizing with but one voice.

Nell Zanatta may be haughty but she is gorgeous in this role, in this scene. Pio is motionless in the wings with the other chorus mem-

bers. Many are weeping despite having seen this scene many times over. His own throat contracted in a spasm.

BRUNA CHIAPPELLI LANDUCCI, TAPE TRANSCRIPTION, 1996

But back to the brattices, that's where my husband comes in. I want to talk about him some more. Remember all that mining law! Night after night and sometimes I was just tired of it, so I'd say to myself, "Well, I'm glad you enjoy it so much." But his mother and I used to listen to it. I had to test him so he'd learn it and I just naturally learned along with him. We'd wait for him there on the front porch when he came home from the night shift.

One time he got the rheumatic fever. We could just hear him coming down the road; he'd just plop, plop, plop—as if each step would be the last one he could manage. And he'd be soaked from the sweats and many a time I would have to help him get out of his clothes, he was just that weak. But that fever, it developed into a real serious case and then he later had to have the open heart surgery, which he didn't make it, of course. He lost his life right there on the operating table.

We waited and we waited. The longer we waited, the more worried I felt. I'll tell you that worry turned sour in me when the doctor finally did come. I can see him, that doctor, coming down the hall, in slow motion it seemed. His feet not even making a sound, like he was floating, but in a way that just scared me to death.

These memories are sticking deep in my life today.

BRUNA CHIAPPELLI LANDUCCI, TAPE TRANSCRIPTION, 1996

I had wanted to talk about Daddy and the mines, but that also brings to mind my Mama, your Nonna—Elisa Gianni in Chiappelli. That's how they would say it in Italy. The woman keeps her own name but now her family name is "in" her husband's family line. I like that way of thinking, not to lose the connections. See I'd be Bruna Chiappelli in Landucci, and that's been true in my life. My sisters-in-law have been close as sisters because we all go to the same church. You know Arlene and Delores of course and do you remember 'Nita? Every morning I'd watch her bedroom shade. It was our signal that she was up and feeling all right. She had the heart trouble just like Tony. So that morning when her shade wasn't up; that's when I knew—even before we went to look for her. [There is a short pause in the tape]

But dear me, I was going to talk about Mama and Daddy! Enough about me; enough now. Basta as Mama used to say—it means enough do you remember that? She used to say it to you, I remember. You were a handful, I'll tell you. You wore her out. If she wasn't saying "enough!," she was saying "aspette," which I'm sure you remember means "wait." Course she was forty or so when she had your mother, so she was already in her sixties when you were born.

Mama helped the family too. Not everybody was literate in those days, and your grandmother made a name for herself in all those little town. She had book smarts. The neighbors, other Italians, would come to her to read their letters for them and for her to write back for them.

One man, Mr. Tirabassi, even asked to her to write his will. He stood at our table, while she wrote. He made lists of his things and whom they'd go to. And there was a long silence: I thought she'd lost her place or forgotten the first thing on the list, so I was about to ask her but—well you could of knocked me over with a feather—Mama just started to cry! I remember trying to pat her back and Mr. Tirabassi apologizing but I could tell he didn't know what he was apologizing for and neither did I.

She said she was thinking about her poor brother, Alveardo, dead at Caporetto in the First World War, and the rest of her family. Now she didn't say this, but she may have been thinking that nothing would come to her. Not that they had anything of value you know, but even for remembering. Mama sighed and sniffed. "Di doman non si è certezza" which means you couldn't be sure of anything tomorrow or in the future.

But all the same, Signore Tirabassi was so happy with her phrasing and penmanship, he said he'd tell everyone to come to her. He gave her a rabbit and that was good news back then. We had so little. She probably made a nice Sunday zuppa with it. Mama said her mother used to say il mangiare è un richiamo, eating is recalling. And this was for sure. When we had meat, it was such a little bit, we'd remember the last time we had meat! It went chopped in a soup to stretch it out with flat squares of pasta made from, well for a big batch it would be 12 cups of flour, 12 eggs, and water to soften. That was the recipe. We didn't always have enough eggs but when we did that dough was as yellow as butter. All morning it would take her to roll it out, then boy, did her arms ache then.

Mama talked about her own mother making pasta. And I can remember clouds of flour puffing up from the table as she worked the dough, or tossed the strands to dry. My mouth could water now just thinking about it! She baked on Thursdays—twelve or more loaves for the week. Beans and bread and a little meat—that's what we ate mostly. "Poco ma buono" which means "just a little but good." And it was true, that's for sure, but I bet it's because when you're hungry, anything tastes good. Course sometimes we'd have to slice the bread so thin that we joked we could see through it. We held it up to look through and say, "Ti vedo!" I see you.

But it was on a Saturday that explosion was. Now I wouldn't have remembered that the explosion was on a Saturday, though now that I think about it, maybe I would have, because you see I know I wasn't at school that day, and Carlo was working in the chutes. Yes, I do remember that.

Now this article mentions survivors, 'This reporter learned that three miners had escaped by way of another, less-known route.' Now that must have been my dad and Pete Corsini! And here's more—you know a little girl must have had big ears because I heard my father say about his scarf— but I wanted something to verify this, someone who

219

didn't know me. 'John Rico induced them to soak their handkerchiefs in water and tie them about their faces.'

So you see, this article verifies what I had said though I remember the story was that my Mama had made such a thick scarf, so it made an extra good filter. And they didn't need John Rico to tell them about needed a filter, had already done it themselves.

Bruna Chiappelli Landucci, tape transcription, 1996

I know you asked how Nonna and Nonno met, but I don't know how they met exactly. Daddy was working maybe in an ironworks, or maybe making charcoal in the same area. He took opera lessons I remember that, but I don't know if that was when he met Mama.

Her family must have worried though because, see, my dad was not a paisani. Now he told me that he had some family in Pistoia, but he was born in Udine. A month after they got married, they came to America.

Daddy said that many single men like Piagi, came to make money to send home. I'll bet you don't know Piagi, he was our boarder when I was about ten; he taught Carlo how to whistle. Carlo would puff and puff after dinner and his eyes got big as cups, his face going redder and redder—he was concentrating that hard. Then Daddy called out for this song or that, clapping a beat, even though Carlo should have been studying his lessons or stacking wood. So it was me that his chores as well as mine! Even his schoolwork, but I have to confess now—I loved spelling so I didn't mind doing the spelling. Anyway they say thousands and thousands of dollars poured from America into Italy in those days. Everybody thought that a man who worked in America had good prospects. So Mama and Daddy? Well…they got married like people do.

You asked me what a typical day was like in our home when I was a child. At home, Mama and Daddy would rise before daybreak to pack everyone's lunch and fix breakfast. After we left for school with lunches. Then she did housework, cooking and sewing like most housewives did at the time. Though she didn't have any time-saving appliances, I'll tell you. Her stove was wood and coal heat. She had a wringer washer or a washtub to scrub the clothes in.

They made their own soap from fat, lye, and let it set until it got hard and then cut it into big hunks. That was what she was doing on the day of the explosion. It didn't end this way on that day but normally she had to heat all the water on the coal stove before she could wash. Once the water got hot, she would shave the soap into slivers and let them melt in the water with bluing. They she would rinse the clothes and hang them outside to dry or in winter hang them in the house. The sitting room was a trap, crossed this way and that with rope. Oh we'd duck under one and another to go upstairs to bed. Carlo would always try to trip or hang one of us girls.

RESEARCH

"The Coal Commission made a special study of 713 company-owned towns. More than 2/3 of all the houses were finished outside with weatherboard, usually nailed directly on the frame, with only paper for sheeting. The houses were built without a cellar and usually perched on post foundations. Only 38% had plaster; 2.4% had bathtubs or showers; 3% had inside flush toilets; 13.8% had running water. Very bad condition—and these conditions described were not caused by economic depression, but in 1922 shortly after the war boom period."

"The natural isolation of the camps, together with their lack of recreational facilities, group activities, reduces camp life to a monotonous sort of existence. True especially for women—there is little for them to do—food is obtained largely from the commissary and required little preparation. The children do a large proportion of the purchasing. Most of the expenditures of the family are made in the company store. Rent, light, heat, doctor's fees, and hospital charges are all deducted."

—Morris, Homer Lawrence. *The Plight of the Bituminous Coal Miner*. Philadelphia: University of Pennsylvania Press, 1934.

Elisa Gianni in Chiappelli, 1924

Dov'è la ragazza? Bruna should be back by now; where was she? The water was on a simmer, thickened with strained grease, the meat set aside for salami. Saturday was soap day to be ready for Monday and laundry. Bruna went to the store—how long ago now? Before Flora ate or after? Four- year-old Alia watched Flora in the next room. Bruna should be back. The window was too fogged to see through, a swipe for a view of the white snow. The path was empty. No Bruna.

She picked up the only piece of lye cake with a rag and began to shave long slivers into the water and grease. Her eyes burned as she watched the long strands melt. The soap was beginning to simmer. The pot was a little too full; she'd have to be careful when it took to the boil.

Elisa saw a flutter over her left shoulder at the window—a small brown sparrow she thought until it revolved, resolving itself into a brown winter-dried leaf. She blinked and looked away. She had ceased to be surprised by the occasional pictures her mind made of movement. When she was small, she would cry out. Like the beetle in her mouth while scrubbing her teeth. Or the dwarf stomping under the water pump. Since her visions were neither sacred nor prophetic, in Villa di Cireglio, she was thought merely overly imaginative. Imagination was not considered a good trait for a girl.

Elisa had sent her oldest daughter, Bruna, for more lye—it was also what they used to wash the wool after shearing in Italy too. Elisa was good at shearing; she could picture their bodies under all that wool; the sheep settled under her touch. Between that and the occasional name-calling due to her oddity of seeing things, it was her chore to take the sheep to pasture. She liked the sheep, their pink tongues dragging across the salt block she carried along. To pass the time she picked herbs and tucked them in her apron, or drop-spindle tufts of wool to finger-crochet, but her favorite game was una scrittrice in cielo—a writer in the sky—a clear sky was like a sheet of paper. She would wave a smoldering stick, writing rhymes in smoke.

The mine whistle blew but instead of its long note of a shift change it was many short blasts— woot-woot-woot-woot! The emergency signal; big trouble! An accident or worse an explosion; Pio! She grabbed her apron to guard her hands and shifted the iron kettle to the cooling pad. Too fast! A boiling wave rose up, rolling over the top of the pan to curve into her scalp, her face, shoulders. The grease clung like coals; the pain so bad it rang her ears. She was on fire, that's what it felt like.

She ran outside tearing at the apron, pulling her dress down, away from her shoulders, falling to her knees to toss snow on herself, finally laying gingerly face down in it next to the bare grape vines twining the post. Where was Bruna?! The babies were alone. She needed Mrs. Keshi, the healer. Madre di Dio! Bruna!

Bruna didn't appear, and neither did the Holy Mother. Elisa rolled over. The snow felt so good. Bruna, when she did come, would find her covered in snow like a fish laid out for sale on La Via del Lastrone in Pistoia. Snow covered her raw flesh like a sheath of silver scales.

BRUNA CHIAPPELLI, 1924

The ice monster on the box of Johns-Manville asbestos shingles had already devastated the homes of the tiny people pictured on Monarch's Teenie Weenie sardines. Bruna liked that word devastate; it was one of Carlo's spelling words this week. He had to spell them and use them in a sentence for homework. Devastate was "day-vah-

STA-tay" in Italian, and because of the Italian word devoto meant "devout," devastated had a sense that the destruction was an act of God. She already had the Red Devil Lye, but Alia and Flora would need to be put down for a nap when she returned, and as they were both squallers, she took her time.

She knew her made-up stories weren't as good as the ones in school. She loved school, mainly because of her teacher, Miss Stewart. She had brown hair and was pretty and nice. Miss Stewart said it was very important for everyone to know the pledge of allegiance and to be a good speller if they were all going to be one hundred percent true Americans. Bruna wanted to be American if Miss Stewart said so.

A big boom and Bruna's hips dropped as if the floor had shifted. The mine whistle went off in a series of short blasts. Something bad! The shopkeeper dropped his newspaper, "Get home, girl," Bruna ran out and a plume of smoke was pushing up like it couldn't go any faster. Chunks of stone fell, pinging the metal roofs. Bruna hugged her head with both arms, the brown sack of lye thumping her neck and left shoulder as she ran for home.

She had to move to the side because all of Shanktown was running the other way, toward the mine. No one shouted; their lips and eyebrows pressed together. A door slammed to her right. Mrs. Sickenberger took one step out, then sagged back against the house. Bruna watched as she slowly balled her apron into her mouth. Their eyes met, and somehow that started Bruna running again.

"Mama!" she ran to the back of the house along a path. She stopped, sliding a little. Mrs. Sickenberger was one thing, but here was her mother burying herself in the snow with her slip showing. "Mama! What are you doing?" Bruna sank to her knees beside her, the lye in the bag dropped and forgotten. She started to tug her dress up, then she saw the skin, wet and red as meat. "Keshi." Elisa mumbled, she sounded far away, sleepy. She was panting as if she had been the one running.

Bruna struggled to knock at Mrs. Keshi's door with Flora on her hip and Alia holding her hand. Mrs. Keshi hunched a bit; she was tying up something in cotton. At Bruna's knock, she whirled, her eyes squinting. Bruna wanted to apologize for sneaking up on her, though of course she had not. Mrs. Keshi leaned out the door as if she was trying to smell her. Bruna stepped back.

Mrs. Keshi assessed and asked "Men are out already?"

Bruna didn't answer the question. "Mama's burnt!" Then she rocked to her toes as if to run back home, but she bit her lip and waited while Mrs. Keshi slung her bag—leather as big as a calf's middle. Bruna heard the clink of glass and metal from the bag as Mrs. Keshi strode out the door and down the path, calling back over her shoulder, "You remembered the children, Bruna. You have your wits." Bruna stopped, surprised, shifting Flora, who was starting to squirm. Alia quit her and ran ahead to dog Mrs. Keshi. Fine. She noticed that Alia was walking so as to bounce her banana curls. Bruna's lips thinned, At a time like this, she thought. She probably wants Mrs. Keshi to say something about her hair.

Bruna's annoyance with Alia was soon replaced with dread for the moment when Mrs. Keshi would see what her Mama had done, but Mrs. Keshi called out, "The snow. That's good, Elisa. Inside with you now but use snow again for pain." Bruna put Flora back in her cradle despite her bawling.

Mrs. Keshi told Bruna to steam a head of cabbage and until it was soft as cloth. Mrs. Keshi put a blanket on the dinner table and helped Mama lay down on it. Bruna wondered if Mama minded laying on the table and Mrs. Keshi giving orders, but Mama was meek. Bruna herself was glad for Mrs. Keshi. Mama's eyebrows and some hair had burnt. She looked wrong, her forehead too large. When the cabbage was ready, Mrs. Keshi told Bruna to take the cabbage outside and lay it in the snow leaf by leaf until the leaves were as icy as the snow. And to be sure to find clean snow, no soot or dirt.

The cabbage leaves got smaller and smaller as she laid them down left to right as if she were writing for school. She'd heard that Mrs. Keshi read the leaves, but what did these pale circles say? That her father was alive? That Mama would be all right?

She began to cry; her nose ran and she wiped it on her sleeve angrily. Where was Carlo? He was never home to help! "Bruna!" Mrs. Keshi called sharply from the door. Bruna stacked each leaf as fast and as gently as she could; Mrs. Keshi had said not to tear them.

Mrs. Keshi smiled at the stack, and gently laid two on Mama's eyes, then broke an egg yolk on both to hold them in place. "The yolk will keep the salve wet and hold the cabbage in place for a bandage. It's her eyes we have to worry about now." Bruna could believe that. Her mother's eyes were now yellow bulging egg yolks against the shiny salve of her scalded skin. Mrs. Keshi showed her how to apply the salve gently on Mama's arm, while she did the other. Mama moaned, so Bruna barely rubbed at all and Mrs. Keshi praised her light touch.

Bruna Chiappelli Landucci, tape transcription, 1996

We would trade for food or yarn or whatever someone had. Back in Italy, in her village, all the children went to school, until eight at least as I've said, but she had stayed longer. To teach Carlo and me Italian, she would write out funny little stories about the neighbors. Boy those made us laugh! But we weren't allowed to tell. Mama had thought everybody would feel free in America. But it was not so free without money I'll tell you, and dangerous too if men were drinking, and if you were Catholic. Well there wasn't anything we could do about being poor or me being a girl, but we didn't go to church. Daddy said that the coal police would put us in jail if they found us walking around without a parent.

At home in Italy, Mama knew everyone in her town, but she said that here you had to worry. Finally she let me go to the store by myself, but I always had to watch and come right back. Payday was the worst, then boyo-boy, I wasn't allowed out at all, Shanktown even to a friend's house. On payday men were drunk and some-

times there would be big fights I'll tell you. When we lived in Heil-wood—that was where we moved our house in Shanktown burned down. It was in Heilwood where I saw two men—Mr. Rizzo and Mr. Panepinto—sharpen knives, big knives like machetes, on the road; the sparks just a-flying! Some from each family—the Panepintos and the Rizzos—were missing fingers! But that explosion was on a Saturday. Normally there was about 150 men that worked full time in that mine, but on a Saturday it was just a few, you know—that was what was lucky. And there was this one part I wanted to read for you…[clears throat]

"John Stone, mine foreman, whose body was reported recovered had refused a transfer to a neighboring mine just one week before. Alfred Stoker, foreman, had several thousand dollars, the savings of a lifetime, sewed on the inside of his shirt."

Well, those stories just break my heart. This one could have been in some other mine. And that one had to bring his savings along with him. No doubt he had no family at home, probably was a boarder. It says here there was even a pastor…

"The cold weather saved the life of Rev. Clare Irwin, pastor of the Methodist Episcopal Church who is a miner on the same shift. Mr. Irwin lives at Lovejoy two miles west of Shanktown, and decided not to report for work Saturday on account of the low temperature."

So you see, there's the wonder of it. So many were killed, but a few lives spared. Now I got to remembering about a little store there. Mama used to send me.

I think she meant to record more because she didn't turn the tape off. What followed were twenty minutes or more of the sound of cars passing by the house and Aunt Bruna cooking in the kitchen. I could follow the progress: she got out a pan, bowls. The refrigerator door opened and closed a few times. Ticking—she turned on the gas burner on the stove. She hummed. Chopping then sizzling and just before the tape stopped, the electric beater.I imagined a chicken breast with onions and mashed potatoes.

RESEARCH

... "100 percent Americanism became after 1920…a narrow racial definition of true citizenship, defining white Protestant stock as "American" and all others as "alien[s]" to be assimilated or resisted.…The Second Ku Klux Klan was not simply a white supremacist organization but also inveighed against Roman Catholics, Judaism, bolshevism,…any threat of modern society. …[The] immigration restrictions of 1924 …[was] aimed at Eastern and Southern Europeans, Asians, and Africans."
> —Gordon, Colin. Major *Problems in American History, 1920–1945*. Major Cengage Publishers, (1999) P. 151

PIO CHIAPPELLI, 1924

Pio remembered a room in the No. 5 left heading where Stone had given someone hell for coming too close to the room in the heading above. Pio thought if they did break through to the next heading, they might find the aircourse for fresh air to stay alive.

They heard a shout: Ches Williams, an American, and Ed Matolik—a Slav and Catholic. Blew them right off their feet, Williams said. Pio and Pietro nodded. Then he asked, "Where's Donahue?" Pio and Pietro exchanged a glance before saying they hadn't seen him. Williams didn't like their plan.

"Aircourse is too narrow. The explosion will have them caved in. Never make it. I'll take my chances in the main haulage line, try to gather up any others. Follow me."

There was a pause; no one said anything or moved. Then Pio pulled out his knife. Williams and Matolik tensed; Pio opened his palms, looking them in the eyes, then cut his wool scarf and dipped the four pieces in his lunch pail water. "You cover you face…the damp." Matolik took his piece and said he'd go with Pio. Williams cursed, "Die with the wops then." Williams threw down the scarf and went the opposite way.

They found the place to break through to No. 5. The ceiling was so thin it had already buckled from the explosion. It took only thirty strikes with their picks to clear a hole large enough for them to wriggle through. This heading would get them to the aircourse but when they jogged away from the main haulage line they found that Williams was right. The aircourse had collapsed and was blocked by fallen rock. Then they checked the other end of the heading, the way back to the main haulage line, and it was blocked by rock as well. Pietro sagged against the wall, and began to cry, "Poor Aggie!" Matolik said they should go back.

"Aiutilo! Help me clear it!" He turned to Pietro, "Why cry for her? She'll be alive!" Then to Matolik. "Here!" He handed Matolik a pick. "While we have the breath."

THE FAMILY REUNION, 1996

The bowl of soup was too full. I sat slowly, incrementally relaxing my shoulders and bending my knees, looking only at the bowl—no spill. I checked the display of articles and mining documents. Aunt Bruna was sitting next to it, reading from the stacks of newspaper articles and mining bureau documents.

I was eating the old way, starting with the soup, though it wasn't quite the same. Chicken broth—sure—with strands of meat cut in one-inch lengths and cooked so long as to fall apart into fibers. Disks of carrot and finely cut kale for color, but the pasta was Acini de Pepe from a box. In my childhood, Nonna made the pasta in a huge bowl, I called it the "Big Belly," and she joked that the dough would make me nice and round like a beautiful woman. Then she rolled it with a cylinder of wood as long as my leg until the dough stretched wider than my two arms could reach. Then she would roll it like a sleeping bag and slice disks from the end, then chop the disks into tiny squares for soup.

If a piece of dough weren't perfect, she'd call, Mia rondinella, "my little swallow." I would tilt back my head and open my mouth to receive the offending piece of dough. In Italian rondine is a swallow, as in the bird, but Nonna liked the double meaning. To dry the dough, Nonna tossed the squares in the air, causing great puffs of flour, shouting "boom-pala!" with each toss.

The soup, then the pasta, then the salad, and finally dessert. Aunt Bruna was still reading with a plate in her lap. I chose a plain cake because of the whipped cream icing, and sat down next to one of my first cousin's daughter and grand-daughter. We reviewed how pretty her dress was and how much she'd grown. Her mother, Val, complained that she was a finicky eater. "Maybe she'd like cake," I offered. I forked a bit and held it up to the toddler's face. She looked at it, looked at me, her expression serious. Then she opened her mouth for the bite, her lips closing over the fork. Both cheeks puffed out as she chewed. Her mother gasped in surprise. I tried another bite. She accepted it, just as seriously again. Val laughed in amazement. I forked over bite after bite, and finally Val whisked off the baby to tell her husband. My eyes welled, and I felt something better than joy fluttering just under my left collarbone. I sighed, and nearly choked on a short elated giggle.

I didn't bring the stories; Bruna would be in a fury over them. I knew her well: she valued resourcefulness not creativity; she wanted facts not a fabrication. The truth was always simple and singular. I knew she loved me—all of us. I also knew that she kept—specifically for me—her own list of my flaws. The stories would dredge it all up and she would have to say every item on the list.

This is how it would happen:

Aunt Bruna would be in a lawn chair, bent over one of my drafts. She would be sweating and looking a little gray around her mouth. She would look up sharply, and when she saw that it was me, she would glare. This is what she'd say:

"Three things I want to say about this story. Three things! First! What's this with your grandfather? He would never have walked out on us! How could you even say such...such slander! That's what it is, just slander! Second! You make your Nonna look like a crazy person! Seeing things that aren't there. And third! You make me look like a traitor! 100 percent American!

"What? What do you know about this? You think this is your story to tell? This is not your story. No, it isn't. You're going to let other people read all these lies? To make all the world that think that Daddy was that kind of a bum? To make all the world think that we're crazy? To make all the world think that I cared more what a teacher said? Not while I'm walking and breathing, I'll tell you."

She would struggle to her feet to make a grand exit. I would hold her arm to steady her. She'd take a deep breath. "I just wanted the proof, not the rest. You—always with the stories, you! Never paying attention when we're trying to teach you something, always rushing through to finish so you could get to your books." She would struggle to step away from me, but she'd need support. To cover it, she'd turn back. Sweat would bead above her upper lip. "Stories?! When are going to do something real? What help are you?" She would stand toe to toe, and since she was the taller, she'd loom for the effect of physical threat. "Look at your own mother! How do you think she's managing with your father so sick with the cancer? And what will happen to her when he dies? Where will she go when she's spent everything they've saved on doctors? What do you know about that?"

Again she would turn to leave, and by this time, her oldest son would quickstep it over, seeing that I was getting the royal talking-to. She would continue because she hadn't said it all yet, there was yet the biggest fault of all. She wouldn't rush because this is her big point; this is number one on the list.

"Oh no, not you. You don't see what is plain in front of your face! Always in those stories you are; that's the trouble with you. Always in your head and never looking out. Now I felt bad for you after you lost the baby. That's something I know about. But that's over and done with and you have a son and your husband's two just like I had my two boys. It's time for you to stop your moping around.

Look and see the people around you and how you can make this world better. Maybe that would help you finally grow up! Am I right? Oh yes; I'm the one who's right this time."

Tony would have her then. An apology would be in his eyes, but it would be me who would have to apologize—just like before. I was the traitor. Three things—I knew what three things would set her off.

My heart would be beating in my ears. I wouldn't be able to gather up the pages fast enough. Even imagining it, I could throw up from shame and anger. These things did not happen to me, but they did not happen to her either! The primary source holds the authority, but with both Nonno and Nonna gone; Bruna held the next ownership. These were not my stories to tell; not while she was alive. It would be mine only after she passed, then and only then, would they would become my inheritance.

I couldn't let her read them. The stories were my version, and Bruna wanted her version. I was assigned the tasks and she was guiding the tone she wanted with the tapes. She wanted a heroic slant, documents that revealed worthiness. For me it was the quirks that I found most endearing. I have heard Bruna and my mother refer to Nonno as a Renaissance man, multi-talented, someone ahead of his time. Nonna was a woman fully in charge, fully partici-pating in the support of the family, clever, resourceful, and talented. That was the correct way to present the family to outsiders. Not this.

RESEARCH

"Ellwood Cubberley,...influential Stanford University pro-fessor, argued in 1909 that the highest mission of public education was "to assimilate...those people as part of our American race, and to implant,...the Anglo- Saxon concep-tion of righteousness, law and order, and...a reverence for our democratic institutions and for those things...which we as a people hold to be of worth."

—"Immigrant Education." Charles L. Glenn. Encyclopedia of Education. Ed. James W. Guthrie. Vol. 4. 2nd ed. New York: Macmillan Reference USA, 2002. p 1097–1106.

"Anti-Catholicism constituted the most pervasive part of the Klan's nativism and emerged particularly clearly in its efforts to promote 100 percent Americanism in the nation's schools. [especially in the 1920s]"
—Lynn Dumenil. *The Modern Temper: American Culture and Society in the 1920s*. New York: Hill and Wang, 1995, p. 240

Elisa Gianni in Chiappelli, 1924

Elisa dropped into a dream. Her mother knitted in the kitchen on a dark autumn day. A candle on the table, flickered over the yarn and her tilting hands. Ice falls hissing outside—layering ice over snow. Her sisters, Elvira and Pia stood at the door. They pointed at the clouds over the field, the iced wheat with hips of frosted green weeds. A black bird circled above the field. Mama knit, the warm candlelight on her hands. The rows emerged from red yarn. Elisa burned as with a fever and wished for a cool drink. Elvira and Pia stood at the door, they could see her trying to rise. Her mother knitted and knitted; the candlelight on the rows—appearing by the twirl of needles and red yarn—and another row, while Elvira and Pia stood at the door and held out their hands, the skin of their arms fresh and tanned. They waited for her at the door. She struggled to go to them....

Elisa woke to hear Mrs. Keshi reciting the contents of her bag. Small bags and jars lined the table along Elisa's hip and leg. A pause. Mrs. Keshi offered to teach Bruna the old ways of healing. Elisa tried to sit up in her excitement—an honor! Mrs. Keshi turned to Elisa, shushing her, gently holding her down just under her burned sternum. Using both hands she pulled the edges of the cabbage leaves, leaving the yolk in a pouch.

Elisa quickly found Bruna's face. "If you knew the herbs,…. Oh Bruna! What a help…I wouldn't worry…."

Bruna stated matter-of-factly, "But that's not how it is in America, Mama.Miss Stewart says we all have to be 100% Americans now." Mrs. Keshi's face closed above Elisa's, and Elisa knew it was over. She sagged back on the table. Just like her father, always with the fitting in.

Mrs. Keshi replaced the cabbage leaves and egg yolks, still unbroken. "Bruna, go find out about the men."

PIO CHIAPPELLI, 1924

Pio was dizzy. No one talked as they clumsily shifted the rocks. He counted them in an attempt to stay focused. (Don Giovanni has been whispering, Da qual tremore insolito sento assalir gli spiriti! It's a line from his opera at the moment the statue disappears, the earth trembles, and flames rise from all sides. And Pio was trembling too.) He paused, and dropped his scarf. Pietro tried to pick it up; Pio shook his head but held Pietro's shoulder. He moved inward; and the song arose, of course, "Và Pensiero" from Verdi's Nabucco.

Pio bowed his head and found the first note; each that followed felt as round as a hot meal in his belly. He pushed the sound at the rocks as if he could clear them with vibrato. The air seemed strangely liquid with small sparking whirlpools, but the song yearns and yearning is something Pio knows.

Pio sank to his knees, grasped the scarf to his face again. He'd done it; it was as powerfully as he'd ever sung. He could die happy now. Pietro wept, "Grazie, grazie." Pio coughed as if he has swallowed a cup of dirt, and maybe he had.

Minutes later Pietro stood, "Listen!" They heard rock tumbling. And finally a voice, "Hello?" Rico, the bragger, but how beautiful he was! He had cleared a hole at the headway. They dove for the spot, scraping their elbows, bellies, and knees. The Slav went first, and Pio followed Pietro, nearly tangling in his feet. It was a long crawl, and there was dirt to clear along the way. Pio gagged on so much, but finally, fresh air, cheering, and men slapping his back. Rico knew where they were because he heard Pio's song on the surface through the aircourse.

Bruna Chiappelli, 1924

Bruna went to the bony pile. Carlo stood beside a clump of grown-ups with little Joe Poll. Bruna didn't like Joe, he always went around spouting his father's nonsense and now with the explosion he would be right. Bruna caught herself with a slap and a quick prayer, Not too right. Carlo was so black from the chutes that the shape of his head stood out against the snow even in the twilight.

She hurried to him to tell him about Mama and to ask about Daddy. But before she could even open her mouth, Carlo pushed little Joe Poll. Bruna, acquainted with Carlo's fury, stood back. Carlo spat, "Your father is a drunk!"

Joe took two steps head-down to tackle Carlo, roaring, "Is not!" The boys met in a clap of snow and grunts. They twisted, punching in unison. In her best imitation of Mama, Bruna shouted to Carlo to stop. Snow and ice underfoot made every move a struggle for balance.

But there was a shout. Carlo whirled to look, then sprinted in that direction. Bruna gasped, forgetting Joe, and sped after him. Across the yard, there he was! Her father, laughing louder than church bells, loud as the mine whistle.

She ran, and Carlo, before her, was swung up in his arms. She slammed a hug around her father's leg. Pio grabbed her shoulder, half-lifting her from the ground still striding, laughing so loud it filled the night sky.

Four Points

One: The Old Country

"…in Italy…in most large towns and cities, a burial plot can be rented and a gravestone placed for ten, twenty, or thirty years. After this period of time the remains are exhumed and, if the family desires, placed in an urn and deposited more permanently in the wall of the cemetery. Otherwise remains are placed in a communal burial spot in the cemetery....the gravestone is removed and the burial plot is used for a new grave....This practice is due to the scarcity of land in Italy...[N]oble families [were] often buried in family vaults in the floor or basement of the church....Some families had private burial plots on their property."

—Cole, Trafford R. Italian genealogical records: how to use Italian civil, ecclesiastical, & other records in Family History Research. Ancestry, Inc: Salt Lake City, Utah. 1995. 115-6

Two: The Old Country Ways

My mom told me that Bruna was known as "Billie." Mom added that of all her siblings, Bruna had the happiest marriage. I don't know if that is true; the further things are in the past, the rosier my mother remembers them. Before her husband, Tony, got so sick and their subsequent religious conversion, Bruna was a party girl. She and her husband, Tony, danced and drank. Mom said you could count on them for a laugh and a meal. I only knew Bruna as strictly and seemingly unswervingly religious.

I asked her son, Tony why he thought it was so important to his mother to prove that her father, Pio, had survived the mine explosion. He said he wasn't sure that she wanted to prove he was a survivor. He thought she wanted a validation of her memory, without fiction. "Her life was mostly thrown at her. Mom was fiercely protective of her memories, of her reputation—she could never accept the recollections of others if they differed from hers."

Three: Memory is the Old Country

A few months after Aunt Bruna's funeral, my cousin, Scott, (Alia's grandson) sent me a digital movie of a family dinner. He had converted a Super 8 film. I can even remember the filming—the square of six lights was so bright it hurt my eyes. He sent it to my work email, so I waited until lunch to watch it. Everyone in the adjoining offices was out and it was unusually quiet.

After a second, the image settled. Harry, Alia's son-in-law must have been standing at the far end of the kitchen of Aunt Bruna's house. The table was extended and set.

One after another the dead appear. Bruna set a bowl on the table then adjusted it. Aunt Alia, her husband, Rene, and their daughter and Harry's wife, Shirley. The four of them, all gone now, and Shirley looks as young as a college student! Her hair is in a beehive and if she doesn't have on false eyelashes, she is wearing a powerful amount of mascara. She looks like a movie star.

I am rocked back at the sight of my young father—how old would he have been? —barely thirty! The child versions of Sharon and me ran in behind him and right up to the camera, shading our eyes from the lights bright as high beams. My mom followed, chasing us to our seats, plunking Julie-the-toddler on a chair at the table between Sharon and me. She tied a huge dishcloth around her as a bib; Julie sulked. Sharon has one too, but I do not. I look to be eight-or- nine-years-old and Sharon would then be six or seven.

And Nonna, she's walking. She waved at the camera, served the soup; Bruna brought the bread and flashed a sideways smile at the camera.

A jump and some vertical rolls and then Sharon and I were at the piano. We took piano lessons for only a year—mom let us quit after she caught Mr. Elgin shoving a water glass between our fingers so our too-small hands could reach the octave. I assumed we were playing "The Circle Grows Round," a simple duet and the only one we knew. But then there was a close-up of our hands and we were playing "Heart and Soul." I guess we knew two; we finished and turned to the right to what must be applause. Our faces shone. I glanced at the camera to see if we were being filmed.

The film darkened and ended. I was disoriented; my head spun. I took a few breaths to steady myself and I wiped my face and blew my nose. Then I watched it again; my mind filled in a soundtrack to the silent images.

I couldn't get away fast enough and finally, I understood the price. I wished with all my heart I could tell them. In that office on that day during the lunch hour, a trapezoid of sunlight crossed my keyboard as I played it again and again. Of my grandparents and their six children and their spouses, only my mother remains.

Four: The New World

After Bruna died, I had several dreams about her, but this one stands out. In the dream I was standing in my kitchen, probably cooking. Through the front window, I saw someone walk up with a cane. I thought it was my Nonna, but when I flung open the front door, it was Aunt Bruna dressed in Nonna's clothes.

In the way of dreams, I didn't question it and I wasn't alarmed, but she wouldn't walk in, and gestured to me to step out on the porch. I did.

Nonna's black shawl was pulled up over her head, partially obscuring her face. She reached inside her shawl and brought out a key, old and bronze with a blue flame licking around it—the flame was not consuming, looking like the low setting on my gas stove. Without hesitation, Bruna inserted the key in my sternum as if it were a lock and turned it to the left. I looked down with alarm and saw that the key slid in easily, right up the ornate clover-leafed handle.

Bruna smiled reassuringly, and indeed there was no pain but a kind of exhilaration. She winked and said, "righty tighty, but lefty is…loosey!" She withdrew her hand, leaving the key and the lock open. She nodded; she was done. Bruna took my left hand in both of hers and suddenly I stood on my porch alone.

I looked like…I hesitate at the blasphemy, but…I looked like a picture of the Sacred Heart Jesus. Instead of the exposed heart ringed in thorns with a crown, my heart was an old tarnished padlock with a key inserted and the shackle released, a blue flame flickering, slowly exposing something beneath.